T.F.M.

The attack on the stage-coach

(*See Chapter 16*)

THE
FIGHTING MARSHAL

The Story of Wyatt Earp

by
JEFF JEFFRIES

COLLINS
LONDON AND GLASGOW

This Impression 1959

PRINTED AND MADE IN GREAT BRITAIN BY
WM. COLLINS SONS AND CO. LTD.
LONDON AND GLASGOW

CONTENTS

INTRODUCTION

IT WAS 1865. The American Civil War was over, and from every corner of the Union men turned their eyes towards the vast unfenced acres of the western territories.

Here roamed the buffalo in untold millions, grazing contentedly on the rich grasslands that had been their home for generations. Here too lay fertile sheltered valleys which had yet to feel the bite of a settler's plough. Even the barren cactus lands held secret, hidden wealth beneath their bleak forbidding contours; gold and silver awaited the prospector's pick and shovel, and copper ore gleamed dully in the mountain gorges.

Weary of war and destruction, the soldiers of both armies laid down their arms and headed West to try their luck. Families packed up their homes and rounded up their livestock for the long trail into the State of Kansas and the wild lands that were soon to be the States of Nebraska, Colorado and the Dakotas. On horseback, or in heavy Connestoga wagons drawn by mules or oxen, they came with but one thought—to start a new life far from all memory of war.

But with them came the riff-raff of two continents whose only faith was in the six-guns at their hips, and in the sureness of their aim.

These men had scant regard for law and order. They revelled in the wild violence of the rail-head cow-towns, where the Texan cowboys flocked to spend their hard-earned dollars in one mad round of pleasure at trail's end. They drank and gambled and fought, from Abilene to Dodge, and from Kansas City to Witchita. They gathered in gangs to prey upon the freighters and the stage coaches ; to steal horses and to rustle cattle ; and everywhere they went they subjected the decent settlers to a reign of terror that has rarely been equalled in the history of America.

These were the men the Law strove hard to subdue—matching violence with violence, and gunplay with gunplay. Fighting marshals were appointed—recruited from the most famous gun-fighters in the West—but they were powerless against such overwhelming odds.

Until one day in 1873 a stranger rode in from the buffalo ranges. His name was Wyatt Earp.

CHAPTER ONE

TROUBLE AT ELLSWORTH

THE old man's eyes were bulging out of their sockets with excitement as his companion counted the money. In all the years that he had travelled the West, from Texas to the Canadian border, and from Kansas City to California, he had never seen so much hard cash stacked up within reach of his calloused hands before. He had long since forgotten the wad of chewing tobacco tucked in his cheek, and the glass beside him lay untouched as he watched the piles of gold and silver coin fill the table top to its very edges.

" It just ain't sense ! " he kept muttering to himself. " That buyer must've made a mistake."

The younger man chuckled at his friend's amazement, but his swift, efficient fingers didn't pause for a second until the last coin had been removed from the leather bag and stacked with the others.

" Buyers don't make that kind of mistake, Cherokee," he grinned. " The tally's correct to the dollar. Half that little lot is yours and the rest is mine, and all we owe for is the stabling for the mules, and a sack or two of oats."

9

Cherokee Watson sat back with a sigh and spat contentedly into the brass cuspidor ten feet away.

"An' all that from buff'lo hides! If that don't beat all. An' to think them know-all hunters told you your ideas were crazy," the old man went on. "Why, son, we've taken as many hides as the best of 'em, and a full five times cheaper."

Wyatt Earp couldn't resist a sly dig at his partner. "I seem to recall they weren't the only ones who thought I was crazy, Cherokee," he said dryly. "Didn't *you* tell me any man who undertook to do the shooting *and* help with the skinning as well was nothing but an ignorant, addle-headed greenhorn? Remember?"

Cherokee Watson snorted indignantly. "Never said nothin' o' the kind, Wyatt," he blustered. "I might've tried to kinda calm you down a mite, in case you got too all-fired big for your britches. But I knowed as well as you that there weren't no sense in runnin' a team o' skinners when we could do it all atween us."

"You lying old varmint," his partner laughed, the affection in his voice belying the harshness of his words. "Let's just agree it's been a good season, and leave it at that."

"Suits me, son," Cherokee nodded contentedly.

It certainly had been a good season for the

two hunters. Equipped with merely a four-mule team, a heavy freighting wagon, and two good riding horses, they had left for the buffalo grounds in early October. And now, only four months later, they were back in Kansas City with a higher daily average of kills than any other hunters they had met. Some men claimed and proved that they had killed well over a hundred buffalo in a day, and it had taken five skinners all their time to keep pace with the work of sun-drying the hides. But just as readily these same hunters had agreed that there were days on end when they had been unable to claim even one kill, and Wyatt Earp's average daily score of over twenty head seemed unbelievable to them.

" I'll never forget that Billy Tilghman's face when he saw your tally," chuckled Cherokee. " I thought he was goin' to have a fit. An' when he looked in the wagon an' saw you weren't tellin' no lies, he looked real green with envy."

Wyatt Earp nodded happily at the memory. " But what about Wild Bill ? The day I told him I was going to hunt buffalo with a shotgun instead of one of those awkward great Sharpe's rifles, he just gave me up for lost and wouldn't discuss it any more."

It was true. Wild Bill Hickok himself was responsible, indirectly, for their profitable venture. " There's money in buff'lo hides, an' meat as well, young Wyatt," he told the tall, serious-faced young man that fall in Kansas City. " You go get yourself a Sharpe's rifle an' four-five skinners. At anythin' from two to five dollars a head you'll have a good stake in your pocket afore the winter's out."

But the idea of a hunter going into a herd on foot armed only with a twelve-gauge shot-gun had appalled him. " Son, you don't know what you're talkin' about," he retorted. " You'll be trampled to death at the first shot."

But Wyatt Earp's theory *had* worked—beyond even his wildest dreams. Not once had he been in danger, and the amount of money left over after all expenses were paid would be more than enough to set him up in any business he chose to consider. And he was barely 25 !

He got to his feet and stretched lazily. He caught sight of his reflection in the gilt-framed mirror above his partner's head, and noted with a sense of satisfaction that the moustache he had sported out on the plains had developed into a fine luxuriant growth. It made him look years older, he thought, which was just as well. He was becoming a little tired of being called " Son " and " Youngster " by the men he met in his travels.

" Well, Cherokee," he said as he caught the old man's eye. " What do we do now ? The new season won't start till the fall, so we've got a spring and summer ahead of us, and money to spend. Got any ideas ? "

" Nothin' particular," grunted his partner. " Exceptin' gettin' out o' these stinkin' buckskins and into decent broadcloth for a change. An' I reckon I might have a try at one o' these hot baths the landlord was tellin' me about. I smell so all-fired like a buff'lo myself, I'm afraid some itchy-fingered hunter might take a shot at me in the dark ! "

Wyatt Earp laughed. " That's not a bad idea, Cherokee," he agreed. " But, while you're cleaning up, sort out what you think about heading up into the cattle country and trying our luck."

" No need to bother about the bath nonsense," Cherokee answered at once. " When do we start ? "

" What ? You mean right here and now ? Why man, we've only been in town a few hours ! "

" Mebbe, Wyatt. But you don't know me as well as I know myself. If I stay in town overnight I'll sure enough end up in a poker game, an' there's a sight too many fast-dealin' rogues around this town for my likin's. The time to be interested in cattle is when you've got money to start a herd. To-morrow may be too late ! "

" But we don't even know where we're going ! "
Wyatt Earp protested.

" Ellsworth Township. That's the place, son.
The railroad's just got through, an' the whole
place is boomin' by all accounts. You go get
the hosses, and I'll be right with you."

" But what about your bath, Cherokee ? "

" That can wait," said the old man with a
grin.

The coming of the railroad had changed
Ellsworth Township from a collection of sod-
houses—built of prairie turf and roofed with
tin sheets—to a thriving cattle-town. Within
months of the construction of a railhead depot
the cattle drovers arrived with their herds of
bawling Longhorns from the Texas ranges :
and with the arrival of the cattle came trouble.

Wild young cowboys filled the streets with their
noise and boisterous horseplay. They flocked
into the newly-built saloons and dance halls,
swaggering with their own importance as they
jingled a full year's pay in their pockets. They
demanded the best the township could offer
in the way of entertainment, and they were
prepared to pay for it. But woe betide the
Northerner who stood in their way, or objected
to their boasting talk. Hadn't they raised the
finest beef in America ? Weren't they hardened
cattlemen who had weathered the long and

gruelling Chisholm Trail all the way from Texas to Kansas, from the Rio Grande to the Indian Nations? And weren't they better men than any gol-durned Northern Yankee? Yes, Sir!

That was their attitude as they hurrahed the township, fighting among themselves or ganging up to terrorise the local people. They laughed at the local ordinance which demanded they remove their gun-belts on arrival in town, and just to show what they thought of the marshals and peace officers who tried to enforce such ordinances, they ran the lawmen out of their own town to the roar of a hundred .45's.

This was the scene that greeted Wyatt Earp and Cherokee Watson as they rode up past the depot and reined to a halt before the Grand Central Hotel on Main Street.

"Best reserve ourselves a room while the going's good, Cherokee," suggested the younger man, nodding to indicate the rows of patient cattle-ponies lined up along the hitching rails on both sides of the rutted plaza.

"I can see us sleepin' on the sidewalk with all this crowd in a one-horse place the size o' Ellsworth," grumbled Cherokee, as he swung down from his horse and stretched his aching back.

Wyatt joined him, and together they crossed the plaza and mounted the raised sidewalk leading to the hotel. Before they reached the door a violent outburst of angry yells broke from Brennan's Saloon a little farther up the block and half a dozen men burst through the bat-wing doors and out into the street like startled rabbits.

" Looks to me like things are livenin' up," chuckled Cherokee, peering eagerly at the saloon. " D'you think there'll be any shootin', Wyatt? Ain't seen a good gunfight in months ! "

" You'll see more than enough gunplay before we leave Ellsworth if I'm any judge," the young man told him. " This town is buzzin' like a beehive. Come on, let's see about that room."

The hotel-keeper greeted them sourly.

" There's only one room left in the place, stranger," he told Wyatt. " It's way up in the attic. Take it or leave it. It's the only room you'll get in town to-night."

" We'll take it. Where are your stables ? "

" At the rear, Mister. You'll have to find anything you want yourself. I'm too durned busy to bother m'head about hosses at this time o' day."

" Thanks," said Cherokee sourly. " Thanks for nothin'." He turned to his young partner. " Let's get them hosses cared for right away, afore we mosey along to see what Ellsworth has to offer us."

He was leading the way to the door when the hotel-keeper shouted to him.

" Hey, Mister ! "

Both men turned.

" What's eatin' you ? " asked Cherokee.

" Check in your guns afore you roam around this town," the hotel-keeper told them, with a nod in the direction of the series of hooks on the far wall. " Local ordinance. No guns to be worn in town, by order o' the Mayor."

" Do as he says," advised Wyatt Earp as Cherokee broke into a bad-tempered argument. He unbuckled his own guns and slung them over a hook. As he did so his eyes spotted a shotgun leaning up against the wall in the corner. There was something familiar about the delicately carved stock. He bent to pick it up.

" Better not touch that, Mister," came the voice of the hotel-keeper from right behind him. " That's Ben Thompson's gun."

" I thought it was." The tall young buffalo-hunter straightened up to his full six feet, and both men noticed how he flexed his shoulders. His eyes had narrowed and stern, hard lines were etched about his mouth and the hollows of his cheeks.

" Reckon you must know the gent," said Cherokee.

"I know him," Wyatt answered, and both men knew by his tone that it hadn't been a pleasant meeting wherever it had been.

" Who is he, Wyatt ? The name's familiar, but I'm durned if I can place him. An' what've you got agin him anyway ? "

Wyatt Earp's light-blue eyes were ice-cold as he answered.

" I saw him kill a man in Kansas City, Cherokee," he said quietly. " In cold blood— with that same shotgun."

" That's the man, Mister," agreed the land-lord. " They say he's chalked up twenty killin's in five years, an' his brother Bill is well nigh as bad. They're both in town—an' stayin' in my hotel, more's the pity."

" Where are they now ? " asked Cherokee, with a nervous glance behind him.

" Over in Brennan's Saloon. There's a big poker-game goin' on there, an' both the Thompsons are playin'. From what I hear they're losin' a pile o' money, an' gettin' nastier every minute."

Wyatt Earp was about to ask another question when a further outburst sounded from the direction of Brennan's. They heard the sound of heavy footsteps thudding down the sidewalk at a run, and next moment the door of the Grand Central was flung open to reveal a great bull-like man in his early thirties.

The newcomer stood swaying slightly on his feet and they saw the crazy look in his red-rimmed eyes. A bushy black moustache sprouted from his upper lip, and his thinning hair was dark with grease.

" Get outa my way ! " he snarled. " I'm goin' to get me a gun."

He lurched into Cherokee, sending him flying against the wall as he lost his balance, and before any of them could say a word he had snatched up the shotgun and stumbled out into the street.

" Talk of the Devil," said Wyatt as the three unarmed men watched the killer's drunken progress across the plaza.

" What goes on ? " Cherokee inquired angrily, but neither of his companions bothered to answer. They were too intent on watching the drama being played out within yards of the Grand Central's porch.

A second man ran to meet Ben Thompson, and by his features they needed no telling that this was his brother Bill. Together they stood in the centre of the plaza and yelled threats and insults at unseen men inside the saloon.

" Come out an' fight, you yellow-livered cowards ! " roared Ben Thompson, waving the shotgun high above his head. " Come out an' fight or do I have to blast you out with buck-shot ? "

From every doorway men poured into the street, taking care to keep well out of the line of fire, until it seemed that every man in Ellsworth had gathered to watch the outcome of the

threatened shooting. But no move was made
from within the silent saloon in spite of the continued challenges of the drunken killers.

"Where are the marshals?" Wyatt Earp
asked irritably. "Doesn't the Law make any
attempt to clean up trouble makers like those
two range rats?"

As though in answer to his question a short,
stocky man shouldered his way towards them
through the crowd. His bearded face clearly
showed the strain he was undergoing, and Wyatt
wasn't surprised to see a Sheriff's star pinned to
his shirt.

"What's the trouble about?" he asked anxiously of Wyatt, but it was a lounger close to
them who answered.

"One o' the townsfolk was playin' poker with
the Thompsons an' they was a-pickin' on him all
the time. He got real mad an' slapped Bill
Thompson's face. I guess that's just plain
suicide in any language."

"Is he still in there?"

"No, sir! That hombre had sense. He
disappeared out o' the back the minute the
Thompsons ran to get their guns. I was in
there too—that's how I know what happened."

"Do the Thompsons know this?" asked the
Sheriff.

"I guess not."

"Then it's about time someone told 'em."

Without another word the quiet-spoken Sheriff stepped out into the open and made for the Thompsons.

" That man's got guts," said Wyatt sincerely.

" Sure has," agreed Cherokee. " Rather him than me."

" It's all right, boys," came the Sheriff's voice as he approached the brothers. " There ain't nobody in there. They all slipped out at the back."

Ben Thompson swung his shotgun towards the little man. " Keep outa this, Sheriff," he warned, but the little man repeated his information and didn't pause until he was right up with the brothers.

" Come along in an' have a drink with me, boys," the onlookers heard him say. " Shootin' up an empty saloon won't get you anywhere."

Ben Thompson glowered at the man for a full minute, then, suddenly, without any warning, put back his head and roared with laughter.

" Come on, Bill. Let's have a drink on the Sheriff. It ain't everyday we get a chance o' drinkin' with the Law."

A long drawn-out sigh of relief sounded from the crowd as the three men vanished into the saloon.

" Phew ! " said Cherokee Watson. " That Sheriff had the luck o' the Devil himself."

Wyatt nodded. " I only hope he manages to

get hold of that shotgun," he said soberly. "All the time those men are armed there s no knowing what they might do."

But all seemed quiet within the saloon as the Thompsons enjoyed the unexpected hospitality of the Sheriff, and presently the onlookers drifted back to the neighbouring saloons, or to their stores and houses.

" I'm goin' round the back with the hosses," Cherokee announced, and stumped off to the hitching rail to untie the two geldings. Wyatt Earp still stood on the porch of the hotel, and his eyes were worried.

" I'm staying here for a while, Cherokee," he called to the old man. " This affair isn't over yet by a long way. When Ben Thompson's in this mood there's no holding him."

" Then stay clear o' gunshots, son," warned his partner as he led the horses away. " You've got to keep your health an' strength so's we can get into the cattle business, don't forget ! "

But Wyatt was in no joking mood. In spite of his youth he had seen more than enough gunplay since he came West with his parents in the summer of '65—and now, after nearly eight years of working his way from town to town and camp to camp in search of adventure and profit, his sixth sense warned him of trouble long before it started.

It was no idle curiosity that held him on the

porch with his eyes on the door of Brennan's Saloon. He was no gawping time-waster with nothing better to do than stand at street corners and wait for sensational happenings. Ever since his first taste of action, when the Sioux streamed down from the hills to attack his father's wagon-train, he had studied men who wielded firearms.

A peaceful man by nature, and reared by his lawyer father to have a wholesome regard for Law and Order, Wyatt had developed an intense interest in how such men as the Thompsons could be tamed and brought to heel. So far no Marshal or Sheriff had succeeded. Perhaps the Sheriff of Ellsworth County had found the answer? If so, then Wyatt's own ideas were wrong. To his mind it was strength that was needed—not compromise and appeasement. It would be interesting to see which theory was right.

These were the thoughts that puzzled their way through his brain as he leaned against the wooden wall and waited with the same calm patience that Cherokee had grown to admire way out on the buffalo range, when the great herds ambled towards their wagon with painful slowness.

He hadn't long to wait.

CHAPTER TWO

" THROW DOWN YOUR GUN ! "

CHEROKEE reappeared from the alleyway between the saloon and the hotel, just at the very minute that the Sheriff stepped out of Brennan's—alone.

" How are the boys behavin' ? " queried the old man.

" They've steadied down now," the Sheriff told him. " I don't think we'll have any more trouble from them to-night." He mopped his damp forehead with the sleeve of his shirt and sank on to a wooden bench against the wall of the Grand Central. " I don't want to go through that again," he said with feeling to nobody in particular.

Wyatt Earp stepped forward. " Did you get hold of their guns ? " he asked.

The Sheriff looked up and shook his head. " No, son. I tried but there wasn't a hope."

" Then there'll be more to come," the young man stated grimly.

He had barely uttered the words when Bill Thompson appeared at the door of Brennan's. In his hands lay his brother's shotgun, fully cocked.

24

He stood there, lurching drunkenly in the red glow of the setting sun. He straightened up as he caught sight of the Sheriff, who had risen to his feet at first glimpse of the liquor-crazed killer.

Bill Thompson let loose a wild yell of triumph. " I'm goin' to get me a Sheriff ! " he screamed and fired both barrels point blank at the lawman. The buckshot struck the Sheriff with such force that he jerked backwards into Wyatt Earp's arms.

Wyatt stood rooted to the spot with horror. It had all been so quick—and so senseless. His own hat had been snatched from his head by a stray shot, and a yelp of pain indicated that Cherokee had been hit. He needed no telling that the buckshot had performed its evil work. At such close range it was impossible that the Sheriff could still be living. He laid the lifeless form down on the sidewalk, and hurried across to check Cherokee's injuries.

Meanwhile news of the killing was travelling fast through the streets of the township, and the plaza filled with angry men—demanding instant action to avenge the death of their Sheriff. But the men who were so ready to urge others to reprisal were notable for their reluctance to make a move themselves.

Bill Thompson still stood in the same position when his brother ran to join him.

" Quick, man ! " Ben ordered. " Get your

horse and beat it outa town. Take this rifle and let me have that shotgun. There'll be the devil to pay for this."

The killer stumbled blindly towards his tethered horse. He mounted awkwardly, still grasping the rifle his brother had thrust into his hands, and spurred down the street under cover of the shotgun, and the revolvers of a score or so of Texan cowpunchers who had sided with the killer.

One man—Brocky Jack Norton—moved to intercept him, but a bullet smacked into the fanlight of Beebe's Store above his head and sent him scuttling for safety.

Wyatt Earp looked up from examining Cherokee Watson's minor wound.

" You'll be all right," he told the grumbling hunter briefly. " Get under cover. I'm going to see what's happened to the deputies."

He shouldered his way through the crowd, making for Beebe's Store. Brocky Jack made room for him behind the cover of the door, and Wyatt caught sight of a deputy's badge on his vest.

" What's the matter ? Scared ? " he asked scathingly.

The deputy flushed with anger. He was about to retort when a third man entered the store through the back way. He carried a Colt Peacemaker in his right hand, but from the

excitable way he waved it around Wyatt knew he
was unused to firearms, and had little intention
of firing.

" Get out and arrest that man, Norton ! " he
cried as he saw the deputy.

Brocky Norton didn't even look round.
" D'you think I'm crazy ? " he asked sourly.

The newcomer turned almost purple with
anger. " As Mayor of this town I order you to
arrest that man ! " he spluttered. " I pay you
to keep the peace, and here you are skulking in
doorways while a murderer and a bunch of
armed Texans roam the streets defying you."

" Take the weight off your feet an' pipe down,
Jim Miller," the deputy retorted. " I'm bidin'
my time. There's no sense in walkin' into a
hail o' lead. Take a look, man. There's a coupla
dozen hombres with itchy trigger-fingers backin'
Thompson's play. It's certain death to move out
o' cover."

Wyatt Earp had been a silent witness of this
conversation, and now he could contain himself
no longer.

" Nonsense ! " he said angrily. " Any man
with half the guts your Sheriff had would take
Ben Thompson right here and now ! "

Brocky Norton looked up at the young stranger
with a sneer. " That's big talk, kid. I see you
ain't even wearing a gun, so there's no chance
o' you bein' asked to follow your own advice."

But Wyatt returned the deputy's contemptuous glance with a cool, even stare. " Give me a gun and I'll show you how to do your job," he suggested.

The Mayor turned towards him eagerly. " D'you mean that, youngster ? " he asked.

" Of course."

" Then help yourself to any gun you want from Beebe's shelves, and go out there and arrest Ben Thompson. Here you are," he added, snatching the deputy's badge from Norton's vest. " I appoint you Marshal of Ellsworth. Norton's fired for cowardice. Now do your duty."

Slowly Wyatt Earp took the badge and pinned it to the left breast of his shirt. He brushed past the two men without another word and strode to the store's gun counter.

The array of six-guns, derringers, rifles and assorted cartridges that faced him was about as comprehensive as any man could wish to see. There were firearms of all calibres from the .20 of a pearl-handled woman's pistol to the gaping muzzle of a 10-gauge shotgun. They lay on shelves behind the counter, or hung from nails driven into the corner wall—some still packed in the manufacturer's cases, or as yet uncleaned of the heavy layer of grease that had protected them on their journey from the eastern factories.

Wyatt ignored all but the .45 calibre single-action Colts. He picked up a pair of brand new Peacemakers of the latest pattern, but discarded them as too stiff for fast firing. Instead he selected a well-worn pair of Navy Colts. One feel of the hair trigger action was enough— the previous owner had performed a first-rate job of filing to get them to that degree of sensitivity. He buckled the wide leather-belt about his waist, settled the battered holsters to his liking, and made a practice draw.

The two guns handled perfectly. They nestled in his palms as though they had been made for him, and sprang from their holsters with beautiful ease. He made a slight adjustment to his right strap, and speedily thumbed five shells into each cylinder—leaving the sixth chamber of each gun free to take the firing-pin of the hammer. He wanted no premature firing with a pair of guns set as fine as these were.

Well satisfied with his choice, he returned to the door and paused on the threshold.

The two men watched him in silence as he peered out at the scene in the plaza.

Ben Thompson still held the town at bay with his shotgun—defying the townsfolk to start something, or attempt to ride in pursuit of his brother. The Texans echoed his challenges, emboldened by the lack of response. They laughed and joked with him, slapping his back and egging him on to further boasting of what he would do to the first man who showed his nose from cover. And all the time they swaggered and strutted up and down the sidewalk, or in the street itself, with drawn guns in their hands in defiance of the Mayor, the deputy, and every law-abiding citizen in the territory.

" You ain't in any hurry, I see," sneered Brocky Norton. " Gettin' cold feet all of a sudden ? "

Wyatt ignored him. His mind was racing— searching for the answer to the problem he had set himself, and he was oblivious of all but the man out there against whom he was about to match his wits and his speed with a gun.

Wyatt Earp made his decision and stepped out into the open.

The plaza of Ellsworth Township was treeless and entirely without shade. Its surface was of hard packed mud, pock-marked by hoof prints and criss-crossed by the ruts of a hundred wagon wheels. On this late afternoon of high summer it lay parched and hard as concrete beneath its coating of fine reddish dust.

As Wyatt Earp stepped down from the sidewalk, a tense silence fell upon the crowd and every eye turned towards him.

He paused for an instant as he came into full view, his eyes fixed unblinkingly upon the shot-gun in Ben Thompson's hands. He saw the muzzle swing swiftly in his direction and then stop—held rock steady in direct line with his stomach. One false move now and Wyatt Earp knew that he had only seconds to live. He took a deep breath, squared his shoulders, and moved towards the killer.

A murmur ran through the crowd as man turned to man and asked in urgent whispers who this crazy youngster was. No one knew.

" Whoever he is, he's got more pluck than sense," one old-timer volunteered. " There's easier ways o' dyin' than takin' on Ben Thompson."

His neighbours nodded their agreement.
" He'll wait for him to get within fifty yards an' then let him have it—both barrels," one of them stated grimly. But the others weren't listening ; they were far too engrossed in the drama being played out before them.

" What goes on ? " asked Cherokee Watson, irritably, from the bench in front of the Grand Central where he sat and nursed his wounded leg.

" Your young friend's aimin' to swap lead with Thompson," the hotel-keeper told him with a sneer.

" What ! "

Cherokee was on his feet in a flash, his wound forgotten and his eyes wide with astonishment. Above the heads of the crowd he saw Wyatt walking steadily across the plaza, slim and youthful in his white shirt, tight-fitting black trousers, and high-heeled riding boots. A wide-brimmed black Stetson was tilted forward on his head, shading his wary eyes from the the brilliant red of the setting sun, and at his hips swung the polished butts of his borrowed guns, still nestling in their holsters and undrawn.

Cherokee was stunned speechless by the sight. He just didn't know what to do, or say, or even think. In horrible fascination he clung to the upright of the wooden awning for support, and watched the space between the two men narrow.

Eighty yards . . . seventy yards . . . sixty yards. Still no move came from Ben Thompson.

Fifty-five yards . . . fifty yards. . . .

Wyatt Earp felt the perspiration collecting on his forehead. His mouth was dry, and his eyes were beginning to feel as if they were out on stalks as he stared without pause at the hand that gripped the butt of the shotgun. He was close enough now to see the thick, dirt-grimed finger that curled about the trigger within the half circle of the guard. Any move to squeeze that trigger would be telegraphed along the line of wrist and palm and finger, and his life depended upon sensing the slightest movement and acting before Thompson could fire.

At forty-five yards the strain became unbearable.

" Cut loose, Ben ! " came the callous urging

of the leader of the Texan cowboys, George Peshaur.

" Stay outa this, George ! " Ben Thompson roared over his shoulder, his narrowed eyes glinting angrily. The perspiration was pouring down his cheeks and saturating his neckerchief, but still he held the shotgun levelled at the youngster with the marshal's badge at his breast.

And then Ben Thompson made a mistake. He had recognised his attacker.

" What d'you want with me, Wyatt ? " he called.

Wyatt Earp's heart gave a jerk and a surge of relief passed over him. Wild Bill Hickok's advice came back to him in that fleeting instant. " Get a gunman to talk an' he's yours," the ace gunfighter had told him time and time again, and now he was about to prove it for himself.

" I want *you*, Ben Thompson. Alive or dead. Take your pick." Wyatt's soft, even voice echoed round the soundless plaza, but he didn't pause for a second in his steady pacing.

" I want to talk, Wyatt. Stop an' listen."

But Wyatt Earp was completely sure of himself now. He came on. " Throw down your gun, Ben ! " he ordered, abruptly. " You can talk all you like later."

Barely thirty yards separated the two men now, and both knew as well as every onlooker in the crowd that no gunman could miss with a six-gun at that range—let alone with a shotgun charged with scatter shot. Ben Thompson's eyes began to stare. He glanced swiftly from side to side as though seeking encouragement or help from some unseen person. Perspiration trickled into his eyes, and his heart pounded crazily.

At twenty-five yards Ben Thompson's nerve broke. With a wild laugh he threw the shotgun into the dust of the plaza and raised his hands above his head. " You win, Wyatt," he called.

Only then did Wyatt Earp allow his hand to approach his gun-butt, and even now he didn't draw his gun.

" Get back, and stay back ! " he ordered the shaken Texans. As one man the cowboys retreated at the silent threat of the young marshal's holstered guns.

" Come along, Ben. We're headed for the calaboose." Wyatt drew his gun and prodded his prisoner forward, his back turned contemptuously upon the armed Texans.

" Holy smoke ! " Cherokee Watson subsided on to the wooden bench like a deflated balloon. " If that don't beat all," he gasped. " An' here's me been thinkin' young Wyatt was nothin' but a serious-minded youngster. Why ! He's more of a man than any of us ! "

But Wyatt Earp's troubles weren't over yet by a long way. For as he shoved his prisoner in through the door of the jail the crowd surged around him, howling with glee and demanding instant justice to avenge the death of their Sheriff.

Cherokee Watson hobbled over to find Wyatt with his back to the jail door, holding off the townsfolk with drawn revolver.

"I thought I told you to stay clear o' gun-play," the old man grumbled. "I've only got to turn my back for a second, an' look what you get yourself into."

Wyatt Earp grinned. "Come up here and take hold of the shotgun, Cherokee. Try and knock some sense into these thick-headed towns-folk for a change, instead o' picking on me all the time."

Cherokee did as he was asked. Roaring like a wounded lion he flourished the gun high above his head and told the crowd in no uncertain language just what he thought of them.

"You heard the Marshal!" he yelled. "You've seen what he does to men who defy him. Now go home an' stay quiet afore he decides to run you all in for disturbing the peace."

But it wasn't the townsfolk Wyatt Earp was worried about. Out of the corner of his eye he had seen George Peshaur and his fellow Texans worming their way into the crowd. As he watched, he saw the cowboys taking up strategic positions all around him—their leaders pushing their way to the front of the crowd. He didn't need telling what this move meant. The Texans were about to make a rescue bid.

Wyatt thought quickly. In a flash he had jumped the steps leading to the jail and was face to face with the scowling Peshaur. His Navy Colt was rammed hard into the Texan's stomach.

" There'll be no rescue, and no lynching, Peshaur," he stated coldly. " Get out of my sight and take your men with you or I'll drop you in your tracks."

To everyone's surprise it was Ben Thompson's voice that answered.

" Do as he tells you, George," the gunman advised. " That kid means what he says."

Peshaur hesitated for a moment, then turned abruptly on his heel.

" You haven't heard the last o' this," he snarled. " We'll get even with you, *Mister Marshal!* "

" You won't live that long," chuckled Cherokee Watson happily from the jailhouse door.

CHAPTER THREE

WYATT'S ULTIMATUM

DESPITE Cherokee's snoring, Wyatt Earp slept soundly that night. The bed in the Grand Central proved soft and comfortable after all, for the landlord's attitude towards the two strangers had completely changed. Within an hour of Ben Thompson's arrest a protesting cattle-buyer was turned out of the best bedroom and relegated to the attic which shonld have been Wyatt's by rights, and another bed was made up for Cherokee with a speed that amazed the old buffalo-hunter. Not content with this, the beaming landlord served a special dinner in Wyatt's honour, and announced that they were both welcome to stay as long as they liked at the Grand Central—at his expense.

All next morning Cherokee basked in the reflected glory of his partner. His fertile imagination soon had a whole host of stories worked out concerning Wyatt's achievements out on the buffalo ranges and in the hurly burly of life in Kansas City. When questioned about Wyatt's proficiency with a six-gun his inventions knew no bounds.

" Shootin' ? " he announced to the men who clustered round him when Wyatt was out of hearing. " Man, you ain't seen shootin' until you've seen that boy in action. Give him a six-gun, a rifle, or a scatter-gun an' he'll beat the best you can put agin him. He can hit a coyote on the run at one hundred yards with a .45, an' drive a cork into a bottle at twenty paces—nine shots out o' ten."

" That's really shootin' ! " exclaimed an amazed listener.

" I'll say it is," went on the old hunter, warming to his theme. " I was sayin' the same to Wild Bill only a month or so ago. ' Bill,' I said —him an' me bein' old campaigners you under-stand—' Bill, I've got a young pardner who's so fast on the draw he'd run circles round you any time you like to try him on.' And do you know what Wild Bill Hickok said to me ? I'll tell you. He said, ' Cherokee . . . ' "

" . . . You wouldn't know the truth if you looked her in the face." Wyatt Earp completed the sentence for him as he re-entered the room.

But Cherokee wasn't to be stopped from boasting as easily as that.

" You see, folks," he blustered. " He's just a quiet, unassumin' youngster. If *I* didn't speak up for him, no one else would know just how good he is with a gun."

" He didn't show up so bad this afternoon,"

commented one of the men with a dry smile. He turned to Wyatt then and extended his hand. " I'd like to thank you for what you did for us to-day, Mr. Earp," he said. " We have long memories in these parts, an' you may be sure we won't forget our debt to you. I only wish you had arrived in Town a good deal earlier."

" Thanks, Mister," said Wyatt simply, gripping the outstretched hand. " But I hope you haven't been paying too much attention to the nonsense friend Cherokee has been talking."

The stranger laughed. " We learn to judge men by their actions rather than by what they or their friends say about them," he replied. " What brought you both to Ellsworth, Mister Earp ? "

" We were aiming to take a look at the cattle trade," Wyatt told him. " Seems there's a lot of money to be made out o' cattle."

The stranger raised an eyebrow. " There is and there isn't," he commented oddly.

" How d'you mean ? "

" Well, I'm a rancher, with good grazin' an' plenty o' water, an' nigh on five thousand head o' Longhorns under my brand—but I don't make money. And yet there are cattlemen by the score around this township who have so much money they don't know what to do with it all."

Wyatt was puzzled at the rancher's words.

" Just what are you getting at ? " he asked. He was interested in this open-faced cattleman, and had taken an instant liking for him.

Before he replied the rancher led Wyatt to a table in a far corner of the hotel bar and sat down beside him.

" What I have to say is not for all ears," he began. " Though everyone in the cattle trade knows what goes on they don't talk too loud or protest too strongly when Texans are around." He looked up earnestly, and Wyatt saw the greying hair at his temples, and the worry lines etched deep across his brow. " You see, Mr. Earp," he continued, " what I'm talkin' about is cattle stealin'—though it isn't quite as simple as that."

" Rustling ? "

" Yes, partly, but not all the cattle we lose are deliberately rustled. A good many are picked up by the Texan herds as they cross our land on the way to the railhead. With herds arriving from the south-west every week throughout the season, you can imagine our losses are heavy."

Wyatt Earp nodded with sudden understanding. " Can't you fence your stock in ? " he asked.

" I wish we could," the rancher replied. " But it would cost a small fortune to run wire around our entire range—or even half of it. Besides," he added grimly, " the Texans wouldn't stand for it. They hate wire worse than any one thing on this earth. They won't let anything stand in their path, and if they come across something they don't like they argue it out with six-guns—not words."

" Then what can you do about the stealing ? " Wyatt inquired.

The rancher rose to his feet. He stood there looking deep into the younger man's eyes. " That depends upon you, Mr. Earp."

" On me ? "

" Yes, on you. As Marshal of Ellsworth you have the power to protect our interests against the Texans. With you on our side we local ranchers can insist on a tally of all brand marks at the railhead before shipment east. We've been looking for a man strong enough to enforce such an ordinance for months. Until you came to Ellsworth, Mr. Earp, there was nobody we could trust. What d'you say ? Will you do it for us ? "

Wyatt Earp saw the pleading look in the rancher's eyes as he awaited a reply. He liked the man, and he wanted to help, but his answer was a firm " no."

" You see, my friend," he explained slowly. " I am no longer Marshal of Ellsworth. I handed in my badge not half an hour ago."

" You what ! " Cherokee Watson's voice broke in upon them from across the room. " Did I hear you right, Wyatt ? "

"You did, Cherokee. I said I have just resigned as Marshal of Ellsworth."

For a moment Cherokee was speechless. His mouth moved and his eyes rolled, but no words would come out. "What in the name of all that's wonderful has got into you, son?" he croaked at last. "Resigned as Marshal? I never heard anythin' so all-fired crazy in my life. Why?"

By now Wyatt Earp was on his feet. He towered above the old hunter—an impressive figure of a man even without his six-guns and his marshal's badge. Conversation at the bar died.

"Because Ben Thompson was released from jail this morning, Cherokee. That's why I resigned. The judge fined him one hundred dollars, gave him back his gun, and set him free. I risked my life arresting that man for aiding and abetting a murder—but the Mayor only put forward a charge of 'Disturbing the Peace!' Seems he's too scared of the Texans to see that justice is carried out properly, and I don't want any part of the running of a town that lets a man like Thompson go free."

For a moment there was a stunned silence as the news sank in. The rancher was the first to speak. "Is this true?" he exclaimed.

Wyatt Earp gave him a scathing look. "Of course it's true. Ben Thompson is over in Brennan's at this very moment with his Texan friends. I told him, court or no court, I would give him one hour to get out of town. If he stays a minute longer I'm going after him with a gun in my hand—even though I'm no longer wearing a badge."

Ben Thompson didn't wait for Wyatt Earp's time limit to expire—he prepared to leave Ellsworth well within the hour.

Wyatt and Cherokee took up positions outside the Grand Central as the gunman and a handful of his Texan friends slung saddles across the backs of their horses, and adjusted the cinches.

"Keep your eyes peeled, Wyatt," muttered Cherokee out of the corner of his mouth as the men prepared to mount. "It's not like Texans to high tail it out o' town without a last crack at you."

"I'm watching," was all the ex-marshal said in reply. He leaned lazily against the hitching rail with his stetson on the back of his head. He looked as though he hadn't a care in the world, but Cherokee's experienced eyes noted the way his body was twisted, throwing his right hip very slightly forward. On that hip, slung low and tied down for speedy action, lay his favourite gun—a Frontier Colt with a well-worn butt.

Ben Thompson was first in the saddle. They saw him glance across to where Wyatt stood, then he wheeled his horse and approached at a steady walk. Beside him rode George Peshaur.

Wyatt didn't move a muscle, but his hand was tensed for split second action at the first sign of trouble. The two riders drew within ten yards of him.

Thompson spoke first. " George here reckons you need teachin' a lesson, Wyatt," he stated abruptly.

Wyatt Earp smiled expressively. " He's welcome to try, Ben," he answered without as much as a glance at the cowboy.

Ben Thompson laughed throatily. " That's what I told him," he announced. " But some o' these friends o' mine ain't got as much sense as I have. They've got it in for you, that's a sure thing."

" What are you trying to tell me, Ben ? "

" That you're the best I've come across, youngster. You beat me fair, and I hold no grudge—but watch out for my friends, Wyatt. They won't be happy 'til they've swapped lead with you."

Wyatt's answer to the warning was remembered long after his name was linked with the greatest gunfighters in the West.

" It's time you left town, Peshaur," he said quietly, turning his back on the cowboy and strolling off to join Cherokee Watson.

George Peshaur flushed with rage and his

hand streaked to his gun. But Ben Thompson was quicker. His arm chopped down on the man's wrist in a desperate attempt to prevent the draw. His horse reared high, cannoned into its neighbour, and the cowboy was thrown from the saddle.

At the first movement Wyatt Earp had whirled around. Cherokee's warning cry was stifled in his throat as he saw the Colt flick into sight with incredible speed. A gasp of sheer amazement burst from a score of onlookers on the sidewalk.

"I didn't see it move!" one man cried in disbelief.

But Wyatt Earp held his fire as Ben Thompson dismounted and bent to examine the fallen cowboy, while the remainder of the party hurried across the plaza to join him.

When he spoke Wyatt's voice was as cool and even as ever. "Throw him on his horse and start riding," he ordered.

Two minutes later the plaza was deserted, and only the settling dust gave any sign of the departing horsemen.

CHAPTER FOUR

INVITATION

WITH the departure of Ben Thompson and the Texans, Ellsworth settled down to its first taste of peaceful, orderly life for many weeks. Cowboys still rode in and out of town in their gaudy shirts and wide-brimmed stetsons, but they were subdued and well-behaved, causing no trouble and taking care not to offend the townsfolk.

The storekeepers and traders were jubilant. News of the breaking of gunlaw in the township spread rapidly to the outlying farms and ranches, and trade boomed. Womenfolk appeared on the streets again, bustling about their long-delayed shopping sprees as they stocked up their depleted larders with tinned foods, or selected household goods and clothes without fear of molestation by rowdy, gun-carrying hoodlums.

Wyatt Earp found himself welcomed with warmth wherever he went. Total strangers stopped him on the sidewalks and in the stores, grasping his hand and giving voice to their thanks in simple, heartfelt phrases.

" You don't know what it means to us, Mr. Earp," a farmer's wife told him to his face. " My husband hasn't allowed me to accompany him to

Ellsworth for over a month now, and I was at my wits' end trying to make do with what few supplies we had left. You will be an honoured guest in our home at anytime."

Wyatt stammered his thanks, doffing his hat politely, before taking the first opportunity to escape from the overpowering gratitude of these simple people. The warmth of their greetings gladdened his heart, but he found it embarrassing to be thanked for what had been second nature to him.

But there was no escape for him as more and more people poured into Ellsworth, on foot, in wagons and buggies, or on horseback. Whole families drove in, the children plyiang happily among the sacks of corn and trusses of hay that filled their parents' wagons to overflowing. They pulled up in front of the wide, false-fronted stores and ran inside without waiting to tie the horses to the hitching rail. With excited squeals the youngsters raced each other for the candy counters, where they feasted their eyes upon the sweetmeats and toffees as they tried to make up their minds how to spend their hoarded dimes to the best advantage.

The womenfolk were hardly less excited. They hurried to the millinery counters to see the latest bonnets, or took their turn at examining the gaily coloured bolts of calico, gingham and dimity laid out for their inspection. It was a pleasure to see the brightness of their eyes as they touched the softness of velvets and satins or held ribbons and silks to the light to match their colours.

The smiling settlers and cattlemen left their families to their pleasures while they ordered seeds and tools, or tested the balance of hunting rifles and skinning knives. They gathered in groups discussing crops, exchanging news of their respective neighbourhoods, or talking loudly of prices and yields of corn and cattle.

The Mayor stopped Wyatt as he went in search of Cherokee Watson. " Won't you reconsider your decision to resign as Marshal ? " he pleaded. " I'll give you a free hand to run things as you think fit, and I'll pay you one hundred and twenty-five dollars a month."

But Wyatt was adamant. " The money doesn't interest me, Miller," he replied with finality. " There are better ways to earn a living than by carrying a gun. I came here to enter the cattle trade—not to hire out as a professional gunman. Ellsworth must learn to look after its own affairs without bringing in strangers to fight its battles for it."

Even Cherokee tried his persuasive powers on his friend, but it wasn't long before he realised that he no longer had any power to influence his young partner. The happenings of the past forty-eight hours had done something to the

young man who had ridden in from the buffalo
ranges with him. Wyatt Earp had become a
full-grown man, and a leader of men. From
now on it would be Wyatt who gave the orders
and made the decisions.

" What have you got in mind ? " Cherokee
asked as he looked up from cleaning his revolver.

" I'm going across to the railroad depot to see
what I can find out about the cattle shipments,"
Wyatt told him. " That rancher we met this
morning interested me. There's more to ranch-
ing than just raising good beef. Are you coming
along ? "

" Be right with you," Cherokee replied with
alacrity.

The depot lay to one side of the town, con-
sisting of a single freighting office, and a frame-
built wooden store shed. The newly laid track
ribboned its way across the flat prairie land
due east until it faded into the haze of distance—
leading straight and true to the vast markets of
the central states and the eastern seaboard.

West of the depot the single-track line fingered
out like a fresh-made scar where the construction
gangs were still at work, pushing on with all
speed in their attempts to link Ellsworth with
Witchita and all points West. Along the first
stretch of this line lay corral after corral of rough-
hewn logs, their footings buried deep in the rich
soil to withstand the buffeting and barging of

the frenzied Longhorns which awaited shipment on the next train in.

The two men rode slowly down past the corrals, pausing to admire the best of the steers with the Texan brandmarks clearly visible on their hides.

" Those Texans certainly know how to rear cattle," Wyatt shouted to Cherokee over the deafening noise of the bellowing Longhorns.

Cherokee snorted. " It's Kansas grass that fattens 'em," he yelled back.

Wyatt nodded. It was true enough. Thin, wiry, Texas cattle were raised in hundreds of thousands on the wide open plains and sun-dried lowlands of the south-west. They bred freely, stood up to droughts and winter storms with the tough resistance built up over years of hard living, and fended for themselves with the minimum of attention. Rounded up twice a year—in spring and fall—they coined money for the Texan cattlemen who cut them out into trail-herds for the long overland trek to the Kansas railheads. Grazing as they moved— one drover to a hundred or more steers—they filled out on the journey, putting on flesh and fat their home range would not produce, and by the time they arrived at their destination they were in first-rate condition. A further few weeks of steady grazing on the grama grass pastures of Kansas, and they were ready for shipment as top-grade fatted beef cattle. Texan steers and Kansas grass was an unbeatable combination.

While they studied the cattle their rancher friend rode to greet them. He looked worried.

"I've had word I'm wanted back at my ranch," he told them. "Seems there's some talk of a band of rustlers setting up headquarters in the Indian Nations. If it's true we're liable to lose valuable stock unless we keep our wits about us."

"Sounds bad," said Wyatt.

The rancher nodded. "It may well be, but we're always getting these alarms and there may not be anything to it. How would you and your friend like to ride with me? We may need a little help."

Wyatt glanced at Cherokee, but the older man's face gave him no clue of his reaction to the invitation.

"Where does your ranch lie?" he asked.

"Between here and Witchita. It's some days' ride, but you'll be able to learn something of the cattle trade, and you're welcome to stay as long as you like. What d'you say?"

"What are we waitin' for?" broke in Cherokee unexpectedly. "I feel kinda cramped in a town, an' Wyatt here won't be happy 'til he's shaken the dust o' Ellsworth from his boots. When do we start?"

The rancher shot an inquiring glance at the ex-marshal.

" Couldn't be better." Wyatt Earp told him. " We'll be right glad to accept."

The rancher beamed with pleasure. " That's settled then," he exclaimed. " If you're agreeable we'll meet here at dawn to-morrow."

" Suits me," Wyatt agreed.

" There's just one thing, Mr. Earp," the rancher called as they wheeled their horses to return to the Grand Central to pack their trail kits.

" What's that ? "

" Bring your guns. You may need them ! "

A slow smile spread over Wyatt Earp's face, and Cherokee chuckled happily.

" He's never without 'em," the old hunter grinned.

The overnight river mist was still clinging to the hollows and gullies down by the cattle pens when Wyatt and Cherokee left Ellsworth next morning.

George Ulrick, the rancher, met them where he had indicated. They saw him looming out of the mist, a dignified figure of a man on a jet-black horse with a white blaze on its muzzle. A Winchester hung forward of his right leg in a leather saddle-boot, and his neatly packed bed-roll was strapped securely to the cantle.

" Let's ride," he said briefly, and the two men swung in on either side of him as he shook his mount into a canter past the corrals and out on to the main trail.

They rode in silence for an hour, each wrapped in his own thoughts, and glad of the extra warmth of their blanket coats, but when the sun rose above the highlands to the east and the mist dispersed, the irrepressible Cherokee broke the silence.

" That's better," he grunted as they halted to remove their top clothing. " I feel like a heathen all wrapped up in sheep's wool on a fine summer mornin'."

Wyatt Earp smiled. " You'll be complaining about the heat before noon, Cherokee. How's your leg standing up to the ride ? "

" A bit stiff, Wyatt, and it itches so's I want to tear at it with my fingers."

" That's a good sign, my friend," the rancher told him. " An itching wound is a healing wound. But don't overdo it. If you feel you've had enough of the saddle just let us know and we'll rest up a while."

" Aw shucks ! " came the reply. " This ain't worth worryin' about. I've had worse an' ridden a hundred miles an' more when we were campaignin'. You set the pace an' quit worryin' your head about me."

But in spite of Cherokee's protest it soon

became obvious that his wounded leg was troubling him more than he would admit. When they halted at noon for a meal of coffee and bacon it had become so stiff that the old man had a struggle to dismount. Neither of his companions said anything, but they deliberately idled longer than they had intended over their meal, and that night they made camp as soon as they struck the timbered fringe of the mountainous country ahead.

By the night of the third day Cherokee was forced to admit that all was not right with him.

" Let's take a look at it," Wyatt ordered, and grudgingly the old hunter rolled up his buckskins to reveal an ugly swelling that had already taken on an angry purple tinge. Wyatt Earp needed only one glance at the wound to know that it was infected.

" Where's the nearest doctor, George ? " he demanded.

The rancher frowned. " Back at Ellsworth, or way over to Witchita, I guess. Unless . . ."

Cherokee looked up. " Unless what ? "

The rancher hesitated. " Unless you're prepared to put yourself in the hands of one o' my neighbours. He's no doctor, but he's a good hand at all manner o' wounds and broken limbs. On top o' that he's a wonder with herbs."

As he spoke Cherokee was watching him closely. " What are you being so all-fired cunning about ? " he inquired with sudden suspicion. " Who is this man ? "

" H—h—his name's Samuels," the rancher stammered in confusion.

Cherokee bellowed like an angry bull. " I thought as much ! " he spluttered. " Doc. Samuels—*the hoss-doctor !* I've heard all about him in Ellsworth. What d'you take me for— a strawberry roan ? "

Wyatt Earp burst out laughing. " I guess it's Doc. Samuels or nothing, Cherokee," he grinned. " That leg needs attention within hours."

" Fine friend you are," Cherokee complained. " But I guess you're right, both of you. Lead me to this hoss-doctor, an' let's get it over with as quick as we can." He let his trouser leg fall back into place, and started to mount his horse. " There's only one thing," he warned them. " If he tries to tell my age by my teeth, I'll bite his hand off as sure as my name's Watson ! "

CHAPTER FIVE

DOC. SAMUELS

IT WAS a nightmare journey through the trees in the gathering darkness, but George Ulrick led the way with unerring skill, his surefooted gelding barely faltering. Cherokee rode close behind, his reins slack in his hands as he let his mount have its head. Wyatt Earp took up the rear, keeping a watchful eye on his partner's shadowed silhouette. He saw him slump in the saddle once, and a low groan escaped the old man's lips as a branch whipped back and struck him a stinging blow in the ribs, but Cherokee straightened up again and carried on without complaint.

The moon came up, bright and full, as they broke through into open country. George Ulrick breathed a heartfelt sigh of relief.

"That's better," he exclaimed. "It's plain sailing from here on. We're at the head of the valley that leads to Doc. Samuels's place— another hour and we should be there."

The valley they had entered was a full five miles wide, fringed by dense thorns and nut bushes on the edge of a thick stand of spruce.

Outcrops of jagged rock thrust skywards from the tree-lined slopes, but the valley bottom itself was clear of obstacles, its surface level and the turf springy under the hooves of their horses.

" How are you feeling, Cherokee ? " Wyatt asked anxiously before they moved off again.

" Pretty fair," the hunter answered, but by his tone Wyatt knew he would be more than glad when he could forsake his saddle and rest his throbbing leg.

The moon flooded the valley with its light, turning night into day, and they made good time, shaking their horses into a steady canter.

Doc. Samuels's cabin stood on a rocky ledge to the south-west, where it commanded a fine view of the entire valley. Behind it a wall of rock rose sheer up to meet the sky, whilst below a neat post-and-rail fence enclosed a watered pasture of close-cropped grass interspersed with shelter trees of willow and cottonwood. A shingled haybarn stood to one side and two milk cows and a calf dozed undisturbed beside it.

A warning whinny came from a young stallion who stood guard over his manada of mares down by the stream, and the three horses nickered softly in nervous greeting.

The rancher dismounted and Wyatt helped him release the leather thongs that held a gate in place.

" Best give Samuels a shout," Wyatt suggested,

turning to help Cherokee from his horse. But the words were hardly out of his mouth when a challenging bellow came from the cabin doorway.

" Put your hands up, you thievin' coyotes ! One move and I'll blast you with buckshot ! "

" It's all right, Doc. It's me—Ulrick. Got a patient for you. Can we come up ? "

" Fine time o' night to fetch me outa my bunk. Who's that with you ? "

" Two friends o' mine. Look lively, Doc., we're in trouble."

There was silence from the darkness of the cabin for a brief moment, and then the horse-doctor's voice floated down to them again.

" Stay right where you are, Ulrick. I'm comin' down."

A slight figure appeared suddenly above them, the moonlight glinting on the twin barrels of a twelve-gauge shotgun, and minutes later the man walked down the steep slope towards them.

" What in tarnation goes on, George Ulrick ? " the horse-doctor complained. " Can't your animal wait until mornin' ? "

" The patient's a man, not a horse," the rancher explained.

" He needs your help badly," put in Wyatt Earp as Cherokee winced with pain. " It's a gunshot wound in his leg."

" What, another of 'em ? " the little man exclaimed strangely. " Who are these people, Ulrick ? Deserves all he got I don't wonder."

" You're mighty suspicious to-night, Doc.," the rancher said irritably. " What's it matter who they are ? They need help. If you must know, the wounded man is called Cherokee Watson, and the tall one is Wyatt Earp—ex-marshal of Ellsworth."

" A marshal ! Why didn't you say so ? Of course I'll do what I can." As he spoke the little man hurried forward, laid down his shotgun, and told Cherokee to bare his leg. He took one look at the wound—but that was enough.

" Get him up to the cabin as fast as you can ! " he ordered. " I'll get the lantern lit an' some water on the boil. Hurry, or he'll lose that leg ! "

In the light of the lantern Doc. Samuels proved to be a white-haired man of uncertain age. He might have been fifty, or he may well have been seventy—there was no telling. Whatever his age there was no denying that the bustling little man with the face like a wrinkled walnut was an expert in treating wounds of all kinds. He barked out orders in an abrupt, sharp voice and Wyatt and the rancher hastened to obey.

Cherokee lay groaning on the heavy pine-table

that took up half the floor space of the cabin. His greying hair was damp and darkened with perspiration, and an angry fever flush crept into his cheeks.

Wyatt Earp snatched up blankets and coats to wrap about his friend, while George Ulrick darted about like a chipmunk as he collected logs for the fire and filled every pot and pan he could find with water.

Doc. Samuels picked up a fiercesome pair of scissors and bent over Cherokee's writhing form. For a second Wyatt's heart missed a beat. Surely the " doctor " wasn't going to operate with such implements ? He opened his mouth to protest, but the little man forestalled him.

" Have to slit his buckskins," he muttered. " That leg's swollen so much we'll never get them off." And with quick, efficient movements he cut into the fine, soft leather that encased Cherokee's leg. Right up to the thigh he cut, until the wound was completely free of clothing, and the full extent of the inflammation was visible.

" Bad," the little man observed as he felt the swelling with gentle, sensitive fingers. " There's buckshot still embedded in the wound. That's the cause o' the trouble."

Wyatt and the rancher were watching anxiously. " Can you save him, Doc ? " Wyatt blurted out.

The little man glanced up at him with a quiet confident smile.

" I guess so, marshal," he said. " It's a good job he's a human being an' not a hoss. If he were a hoss I'd have to put him outa his misery." He nodded expressively to his gun. " I should have him right inside a week or two—providing I can find the lead an' remove it."

By daybreak the wound had been lanced, the buckshot located and removed, and Cherokee slept soundly—exhausted by shock and pain.

" What do we owe you, Doc. ? " asked Wyatt as the three men sank wearily down to drink coffee in the first light of dawn.

" Nothin', Marshal," the little man told him.

" But you must take something ! " Wyatt protested. " You've saved his life as sure as my name's Earp, and it looks as though we'll have to leave him with you for a while before he's fit to travel."

But the horse-doctor was not prepared to argue. " Only too pleased to help the Law," he stated simply. " Besides," he added with a twinkle in his eyes, " I charged those others enough to cover a dozen treatments."

" What others ? " asked Wyatt. " D'you mean to say you've had more wounded men around here recently ? "

The little man started with surprise. " Didn't I tell you ? " he exclaimed. " Three men rode in yesterday with lead in them. One had a six-gun slug in his shoulder, another had a flesh wound that was of no account, and the third had lost a finger. Bad hombres they were—armed to the teeth an' desperate. I charged 'em a hundred bucks a piece, an' they paid without a murmur."

" Who were they ? " the rancher broke in.

" Can't say, but there's talk o' rustlers up in the Nations, and I'll bet my bottom dollar those hombres were no lawful cattlemen."

Wyatt Earp turned his head and met the rancher's excited glance.

" Looks like your news was right, Ulrick. And what's more the rustlers have bitten off more than they can chew. The sooner we get to your place the better, I reckon."

" Yes, indeed," George Ulrick agreed. " My wife and son are up at the ranch. I only hope they're safe."

Wyatt didn't like leaving Cherokee behind, but the old hunter insisted. The crisis had passed and he was fast regaining his strength from the ordeal of the night before.

" I'll be all right with this hoss-doctor feller," Cherokee smiled wanly. " Just you forget about me, Wyatt. George will need all the help he can get if these rumours are right. I'll join you just as soon as this leg is fit for travellin'."

At last, content that Cherokee could do no

better than remain in Doc. Samuels's expert
care, Wyatt and the rancher saddled up and
headed out of the valley.

They rode hard, pausing only for hurried
meals and to water the horses. The trail they
followed cut through the woodlands, skirting
the foothills and by-passing all but the smaller
streams. All around them lay rich country, still
fresh and green in late summer, and game
abounded wherever they looked.

Soon after leaving Doc. Samuels's Wyatt picked
up the trail of the three men who had ridden in
to get their wounds attended to. They had
back-tracked along the trail by which they had
entered the valley, before branching off to the
north-east.

" They were headed up into the Indian
Nations all right," the rancher pointed out.
" The line o' that gorge they followed leads
right up to the Badlands."

Wyatt Earp nodded, curbing his straining
horse as they eyed the tracks. " An army of
men could hide-out up there," he stated. " I
was up around the Badlands for a whole season
with the Government Survey party a few years
back. I know it well."

They kept a keen watch for further tracks of
additional horsemen during the remainder of the
journey, but there were none to be seen—nor
did they set eyes upon a living soul until they

came out on the rocky bank of a slow-flowing river.

" My place is just out o' sight, round the bluff to the east," George Ulrick indicated. " The river is my boundary on this side, and there's a bunch o' my Crown Bar steers grazin' to the south if my eyes don't deceive me."

They forded the river without difficulty, their horses finding firm footing on the smooth stones and gravel of the shallows, and spurred their way to the bluff.

The Crown Bar ranch nestled snugly on a level bench of deep alluvial soil above the surrounding pastures. Wyatt admired the neat lines of the frame-built ranch-house, with its barn and granary. A small, but well-tended flower-garden relieved the bareness of the sun-bleached timbers, and gay calico curtains fluttered lazily at the windows.

Riding abreast they clattered their way through the open gate of the home paddock and into the yard. To their surprise no one came to greet them. The only movement was the scratching of the hens in the dust and litter beside the barn, and the bored munching of a dozen saddle-horses in the fenced-off pasture.

They came to a halt and eyed the house and buildings suspiciously. It was only then that they saw the rifle barrel protruding from the half-open door of the barn.

With one accord the two men flung themselves from their saddles, reaching for their revolvers as they landed in the dust.

But there was no danger, for the doors opened wide and a woman ran towards them, still clutching the rifle. Behind her a short, thick-set man with bowed legs appeared, a six-gun hanging in his left hand while his right hand and arm were hidden by a blood-stained sling.

Wyatt lowered his gun and stepped out from the cover of his horse as George Ulrick ran to meet his wife.

" Mary ! Tom ! Whatever are you doing ? " the rancher cried as his wife flung herself into his arms, half crying, half laughing with relief.

" Oh, George ! " she sobbed. " Dreadful things have happened while you were away. We thought you were two of the rustlers coming back."

" Rustlers ? Have they been here ? And where's our boy and the rest of the men ? Has anything happened to them ? " Ulrick exploded into a string of questions.

The wounded man was with them by now, and it was he who answered. " Your son's all right, boss," he stated in clipped yankee accent. " The boys are all alive an' kickin' too, exceptin' Jake Thomas. He got hurt a little—but he'll be all right."

" What about the cattle ? " Ulrick demanded.

The cowboy hung his head and avoided the rancher's eyes. " I guess you won't like this, boss," he stammered, " but somebody's got to tell you. They just about cleaned the eastern range o' steers."

Wyatt Earp saw the rancher flinch at the news. His shoulders sagged and when he spoke there was a note of utter dejection in his voice. " How many head missing ? " he asked quietly.

" I—I—guess around sixteen hundred, Boss," the man stammered.

" That's a powerful lot o' cattle," put in Wyatt softly. " How serious a loss is it, George ? "

" My entire profit for two seasons gone ! " the rancher exclaimed.

CHAPTER SIX

WYATT'S PLAN

WHILE Mary Ulrick prepared a hurried meal, Wyatt and the rancher sat grim-faced at the kitchen table, listening to the man Tom's account of the rustlers' attack.

"The first we knew about rustlers bein' in the territory was a week ago," Tom started. "A posse, led by a United States Marshal, rode in— a score o' men. The Marshal told us they were trailin' a gang o' desperadoes led by Anderson and McMurray, but that they had lost track o' them east o' the Crown Bar range. He said a second posse was workin' its way across from Witchita to link up for a thorough combin' o' the hills up and around the Nations. They reckoned they'd have more'n fifty men between the two posses, an' we'd be safe enough here— but we'd best keep our guards alerted to be sure.

"The foreman kept the boys on their toes, but it seems the Andersons slipped clean through between the posses. I guess they felt so all-fired pleased with themselves—an' safe from pursuit with the marshals ridin' off in the opposite direction—that they couldn't resist a crack at our cattle."

67

"How many of them were there?" Wyatt Earp asked.

"Thirty men," Tom answered, "and all armed to the teeth. Two six-guns, a Winchester, and a shotgun apiece—an' cartridges by the hundred."

Wyatt whistled softly through his teeth, but didn't interrupt as Tom continued.

"I was out after a bunch o' strays when they rode in. There were three of our boys with the cattle. They hadn't a hope o' saving them, but they opened fire on the rustlers an' winged at least a couple afore they were driven off."

"How did *you* get wounded, Tom?" George Ulrick asked.

"Well it was this way, boss. The riders didn't spot me, 'cos I was way up in a draw with the strays. I tied my hoss an' squatted down among the rocks with my Winchester. I guess they got kinda mad at me after a while, an' blazed away so fierce I dursen't move my head an inch. It was a ricochet got me in the arm."

Again Wyatt Earp slipped in a telling question. "What damage did you do to *them*?" he asked.

Tom smiled with grim humour. "Two," he stated happily.

"Nice work," Ulrick complimented him. "You boys have done a good job—cattle or no cattle. I shan't forget it. Mr. Earp and I know for a fact that three of the gang were wounded."

He hastily recounted Doc. Samuels's story of the gunshot wounds he had treated.

The sound of fast approaching horses brought the three men to their feet.

"It's the hands returning," Mary Ulrick told them from the open window. "They've been checking our losses and trying to get an idea of the direction the rustlers were taking so that the posse can be told."

George Ulrick snorted disgustedly. "Fat lot o' good that'll do. By the time we get word to the posse and they get on their tail the steers'll all be out of sight, hidden away up in the Nations. Like Wyatt said on the way here, an army o' men could hide away up there—let alone a thousand or two Longhorns."

Wyatt nodded his agreement. "If we're going to do anything to get back those cattle, we've got to do it right away."

"That's big talk, stranger," came a sarcastic voice from the open door as the range foreman stepped in to report to his employer. "What good are a dozen cowhands agin thirty armed rustlers? Will you tell me that, Mister?"

George Ulrick couldn't resist a chuckle at Wyatt's expense. He was completely unprepared for his friend's answer.

"A dozen men are useless, I agree," said Wyatt. "All we need are two men and a buggy."

They all stared at him as though he was out of his mind.

" Two men, a buggy, and a couple of sawn-off shotguns," he corrected himself solemnly.

The plan had come to Wyatt Earp as he pictured the country towards which the outlaws were heading. He knew that territory well, for he had travelled all over it during the spring and summer of 1870, as camp guard and official hunter to the Government surveyors. He could clearly visualise the many trails that ribboned the highlands, each one leading to deep clefts and gorges or hidden valleys.

He knew full well that any attack by a posse, or any attempt to regain the steers by force of arms, was doomed to failure from the start. A few riflemen posted among the rocks could hold off a hundred times their own number with ease.

It was brains that were needed to solve the problem—not force. Brains and audacity : and he recognised his plan as a winner the very moment it flitted across his mind.

" I know it sounds crazy," he admitted before the others had a chance to speak. " But I know in my bones that it will work—given only normal luck. Listen, while I explain."

As the plan unfolded the men found themselves nodding excitedly, and when Wyatt finished he knew for sure that he had won them over. Even the foreman was impressed by the simplicity of it.

" I'll be doggoned if you ain't right, Mr. Earp," he confessed. " And I guess I'm the man who'll go with you—with Mr. Ulrick's permission. I reckon I owe you an apology for what I said just now, an' the least I can do is back your play."

" What sort of a hand are you with a shot-gun ? " Wyatt asked. " The man who comes with me must act fast—there'll be no second chance with those cut-throats."

The foreman grinned. " Don't worry on that account, Mr. Earp," he chuckled. " I was reared with a gun in my hand, an' before I came to Mr. Ulrick as his range boss I was wearin' a deputy marshal's badge in Witchita ! The name's Jack Burns—you may have heard o' me ? "

Wyatt's eyes lit up at the name. " Why of course ! " he exclaimed. " Young Bat Master-son told me about you. I'm right glad to meet you, Burns. I couldn't wish for a better com-panion on this little jaunt."

" That's settled then," the range boss smiled, before any of the others could protest and volunteer their own services. He turned to the rancher's young son who had followed him into the kitchen to greet his father. " Like to slip over to the bunkhouse for me, youngster ? " he asked with a twinkle in his eye.

" What for ? " the boy asked him suspiciously.

" You needn't go if you don't want to, son,"
Jack Burns told him. " I just thought you might
like to rustle up a couple shotguns and a box
o' shells for us."

The boy's eyes lit up eagerly. " Yes, sir ! "
he cried and he bolted for the bunkhouse as
fast as his legs would carry him.

But his father was not quite so pleased with
the way things were going. " I can't allow you
to go, Jack," he informed his foreman. " It's
my place to go with Mr. Earp. You've done
enough for the Crown Bar in the last few days
without risking your life again."

" I'm sorry, boss," came the reply. " Say
what you like I'm goin'. Those steers were lost
while I was in charge o' them. That's reason
enough for me to insist that I have first chance
at gettin' them back. I'm goin' whether you like
it or not ! "

Seeing that it was useless to argue, George
Ulrick gave in. Instead he ordered the buggy
to be brought out of the barn, checked over,
and the span of horses selected with care. Mary
Ulrick hurriedly packed ample supplies of food
while Wyatt Earp made two special requests.

" You'll have to change those clothes, Jack,"
he said. " You look too much of a cattleman for
my plan to work. Rustle up some store clothes
from your kit, and try and make yourself look

like a townsman who doesn't know one end of a steer from the other ! "

At George Ulrick's suggestion, Wyatt borrowed a smart tail-coat and a pair of sturdy shoes in place of his high-heeled riding-boots.

They left within half an hour, trundling at a brisk trot along the trail the outlaws had taken, happy in the knowledge that behind them, laid carefully within easy reach of their hands, reposed two shotguns fully loaded with scatter shot—their double barrels shortened from the normal twenty-eight inches to a mere eighteen. With such weapons in their hands they knew they were more than a match for a dozen revolver-carrying gunmen—at close range.

The first stage of Wyatt Earp's plan bore fruit almost immediately. Instead of following the hoof prints of the stolen cattle—and taking the chance of losing the tracks altogether should the rustlers adopt any means of obliterating the evidence of their progress—Wyatt branched off across country. Short-cutting towards the Nations they travelled fast along little-used trails, until they came out on a low ridge that commanded a view over a wide area of broken valleys and undulating grassland. Here Wyatt halted the team and surveyed the terrain slowly and thoroughly with the aid of a pair of long-range glasses borrowed from George Ulrick.

" What d'you make of it ? " he asked Burns, handing over the glasses.

Jack Burns took his time before answering.

" I make out four definite trails, and possibly a fifth," he grunted. " From this distance the fifth trail doesn't look wide enough to take a herd o' Longhorns."

Wyatt nodded. " That's about the size of it, Jack," he agreed. " All we've got to do now is cut across those trails until we find the one the rustlers have used. Then we should be right up on their tails. It'll save us hours of trailing."

" Let's go," grinned Burns, and Wyatt Earp shook the horses into motion with a slap of the reins across their rumps.

The first three trails showed no sign of recent prints, and they pressed on, swinging wide of rocks and hillocks that barred their way. At last, some hours later, they reached the fourth trail, and found what they were seeking. The churned-up mud of a spring-fed water-hole told its own story. This was the trail that the outlaws and the stolen cattle had followed.

" Let's get after 'em ! " Jack Burns yelled excitedly, but Wyatt Earp shook his head.

" We're too close to them, Jack," he cautioned. " These tracks were made early this morning— the mud has barely dried out yet. Besides we aren't taking this route."

Burns looked at him with astonishment.

" Not takin' this route ? " he repeated. " Why-
ever not ? "

" Because we need to follow them without
their knowledge. The drag riders'll spot us
straight away if we take this track. We want
to remain in a position to watch without being
seen until we're ready for action. The whole
plan depends on it."

" I guess you're right," Burns acknowledged
lamely. " I was getting impatient."

Wyatt drove on until they reached the fifth and
last trail. It was narrow, winding crookedly
between stands of timber and dipping into sudden hollows with erratic craziness. In places
there was barely room for the buggy to pass and
their progress was painfully slow. When they
reached a particularly dense belt of trees Wyatt
drew rein.

" We'd best camp here for the night, Jack,"
he said with a glance at the lengthening shadows
of early evening. " The horses are tired out and
my belly's emptier than a water hole in high
summer. We can climb up to that point over
there before it gets too dark, and maybe we'll be
able to make out the cattle. I've got a hunch
where they're headed."

" Where's that, Wyatt ? " Jack Burns asked
eagerly.

" The Wewoka Valley," Wyatt told him.
" I know it well, and it'd make a first-rate corral

for those cattle. It's so sheltered they'd even be able to spend the winter up there without harm. I don't mind betting that's where they are making for."

The two men drove the team into the cover of the trees, unhitched the horses and ate a hurried meal from Mary Ulrick's provisions, before setting out on their climb.

When they reached the point Wyatt had selected, they were puffing and panting with sheer exhaustion, and Jack Burns was fast growing irritable. However, the mood soon passed when he followed the line of Wyatt Earp's pointing arm and caught the glint of the setting sun on gunmetal. One of the rustlers stood guard over the trail, high up among the rocks where he could command a magnificent field of fire. He was not more than a mile away, his battered Stetson silhouetted clearly against the skyline in the clear mountain air. Cradled in his arms was a lever action Winchester of the latest pattern—as the two watchers soon discovered when they trained the glasses on him.

" Phew ! " exclaimed Jack Burns. " If we had followed that trail we'd be deader than door-nails by now."

" We still may be," said Wyatt Earp grimly.

CHAPTER SEVEN

THE NEW HANDS

WYATT EARP and Jack Burns rolled in their blankets that night, content in the knowledge that the stolen cattle were bedded down within a few miles of their camp.

They woke long before sunrise and lay awaiting the dawn with impatience.

" If your hunch is right, Wyatt, and those steers are headed for the Wewoka Valley, we've got to make our play by noon." Jack Burns spoke quietly in the darkness, as though afraid of being overheard by the rustlers' guard.

" That's just what I was thinking," Wyatt replied thoughtfully. " We've got to catch them when they are least expecting trouble, and that means as soon as they arrive. In the safety of the valley they'll get careless, and without much need to ride herd on the cattle there'll be a temptation for the riders to take the weight off their feet for a spell. We've got to get close enough to watch without being seen, and then strike fast when we judge the time is right."

So it was that Wyatt and Jack Burns set out at daybreak, working together in complete agreement and with full understanding of what lay before them. Words were unnecessary—they worked together as a team, as only two experienced frontiersmen knew how. Wyatt knew in his bones that Jack Burns would back him to the full in any crisis, while Burns himself had complete confidence in the calm efficiency of the man at his side on the buggy seat.

Wyatt handed the reins to his companion after the first few miles, going ahead to scout out the trail and check on the position of the rustlers. He found the country opening up as he pressed forward, and signalled to Burns to halt and await further orders.

Moving with the quiet stealth of a hunter Wyatt worked his way through the trees to the right of the trail and paused to get his bearings. In the distance he heard the faint bellow of a steer, and then another, and knew his hunch was right. The stolen cattle were well up towards the entrance to the Wewoka.

As he listened for a further check the gurgle of water moving fast over a bar of rocks came to his ears.

" Skeleton Creek ! " he exclaimed aloud. " I'll stake my life that's where they'll halt at noon to water the steers and rustle up some food for themselves."

The more he thought of it the more he was certain that Skeleton Creek was the obvious place for a halt, and from what he remembered it would make the perfect spot for his purpose. He hurried back to Jack Burns and told him what he intended.

"Three hours to go," was all Burns said, grinning with expectation. "Then those buzzards'll wonder what's hit them!"

A full hour before noon Wyatt glanced at the sun and nodded to his companion. "Let her roll, Jack," he grinned, and with a rattle of harness and a crunching of wheels they swung back on to the trail again.

Straight out through the trees they drove, all caution abandoned. They came out above the open plain that linked the two trails, wheeled south, and trotted the horses unconcernedly in the direction of the trail the rustlers had taken.

Out of the corner of his eye Wyatt caught a movement high above them, and was just in time to see a horseman halt behind a large boulder and follow their progress through glasses.

"They're on to us already, Jack," he muttered without moving his lips. "Pull up in a hundred yards and make out you're showing me the territory—like I was a greenhorn aiming to buy land from the Government."

Without batting an eyelid Jack Burns did as he was told, going through a pantomime of pointing out boundaries and indicating water holes and timber. He even went so far as to draw a sheet of paper from his pocket and run his grimy finger over it as though tracing the area on a map.

All the time Wyatt was conscious of the watcher on the hill, but he kept his eyes in the opposite direction without a single glance towards the rustler guard or the hidden steers.

" How am I doin' ? " Jack Burns queried.

" Fine. Carry on for another few minutes, then move off and show me the section down by the trail. Pay no attention to the tracks, and make sure we're out in full view from the creek. I want the whole gang to see us."

Burns did as he was told, and when Wyatt stole a glance up to the skyline he saw that the horseman had ridden off.

" All clear, Jack," he grinned. " I guess we've fooled 'em. They should be halted at Skeleton Creek by now. Follow in their tracks and watch me when we reach them."

" Here we go," the ex-deputy smiled. " I can't wait to lay my hands on that shotgun ! "

They had only gone half a mile up the trail when they caught sight of the herd. The cattle were jostling each other for space along the far bank of the little stream, and more than twenty men sat about on rocks or on the sun-drenched grass, eating from tin platters or sipping mugs of coffee.

The horses reached the fording point a little

to the right of the rustlers' camp, and at a word from Wyatt, Jack Burns urged them into the water, crossing the creek under the very noses of the feeding outlaws.

As they reached the bank, and lurched up out of the water Jack Burns felt a nudge from Wyatt, and saw his hand stealing back to where the shotguns lay. He hauled hard on the reins, swinging the team left, straight into the camp, as Wyatt took a flying leap from the buggy seat with a shotgun in his hands.

" Reach ! " he yelled at the startled outlaws before they had time to move. " Put your hands up or by Heaven I'll blast you from here to Kingdom Come ! "

By now Jack Burns had sprung to join him, and under the menacing muzzles of the shortened scatter-guns the rustlers surrendered. It was as simple as that.

" Collect up their guns, Jack," Wyatt ordered. " Throw them in the buggy. Then tie up Anderson and McMurray while I have a little talk with the others. If they make a move you don't like—let 'em have it."

It was only as Jack Burns completed his task that the problem of what to do with the cattle came to him. He and Wyatt would have their hands full with the captured rustlers, without that additional worry. Left to their own resources the steers were bound to wander off into

the Wewoka Valley in search of the choicest
grasses, and by the time they had fetched help
from the Crown Bar it would take a week to
round them up again. They might even lose a
hundred head or so for good.

But he needn't have worried, for Wyatt Earp
had considered all these possibilities long before
they set out on the trail of the rustlers.

" There'll be a hanging party after those
two," he said grimly to the disarmed men who
stood in a compact group with their hands high
in the air. " We're taking Anderson and Mc-
Murray in for trial in Witchita, and you'll all be
tried alongside them. With luck you'll get off
with a long stretch in the State Penitentiary,
but if the Judge is Old Judge Parker you may
not be so lucky. He isn't called the Hanging
Judge for nothing." He paused to let his words
sink in. Then : " There's one alternative,"
he continued.

" What's that, Mister ? " one of the younger
rustlers asked eagerly.

" Just this. We want those steers rounded up
and driven back to the Crown Bar range. If
you work for us we'll pay you a dollar a day,
and let you go free as soon as the cattle are safe
in Ulrick's hands. But you'll leave your guns
behind when you are released—and Anderson
and McMurray will stand their trial for rustling
and attempted murder. What do you say ? "

" How d'we know this ain't a trick, Mister ? "
one of the men queried.

" You don't," Wyatt answered curtly. " You'll
just have to take my word for it. But I'll tell you
this if it'll make you any happier. Any man who
makes a move against you while I'm around
will have to answer to me with a gun in his
hand. You have my word on it."

" Then I guess we'll take you up on that,
Mister," the man replied with a sigh of relief.
" What d'you say, boys ? "

With one accord the rustlers agreed to Wyatt's
offer.

" Right. Get to your horses and turn those
steers back down the trail. You're working to
Mr. Burns's orders from now on. Go on,
move ! " And immediately, to Jack Burns's
utter amazement, Wyatt Earp lowered his shotgun and ambled over to see how the work of
tying the outlaw leaders was progressing—
without as much as a backward glance at the
remainder of the gang.

" Holy Cow ! You're takin' a chance, Wyatt,"
he spluttered.

But Wyatt Earp only smiled. " Why ? " he
asked unperturbably. " Those fools work for
anyone who pays them enough. There's no
chance of drawing any money from Anderson
and McMurray now, and they know it. Don't
get any notions about there being loyalty among

thieves, Jack. Range rats like them always pick the winning side. We'll have no more trouble as long as we stick to our bargain."

" I only hope you're right," said Jack Burns with a worried frown.

" I am," Wyatt Earp grinned.

Meanwhile, back at the Crown Bar ranch, George Ulrick was growing increasingly worried.

" I should never have let them go, Mary," he said for the hundredth time. " Young Wyatt Earp may have all the courage in the world, but the more I think of his plan the more I fear for them both. It's sheer recklessness, and I don't know what possessed me to agree to it."

Mary Ulrick put a soothing hand on her husband's shoulder. " Don't fret so, George," she pleaded. " Mr. Earp doesn't appear the kind of man who would rush into anything without thinking it out carefully first. From what you have told me of his achievements in Ellsworth, I'd say he was anything but reckless—and Jack Burns is not one to take undue risks."

" But it's three full days now, Mary ! " the rancher protested. " Surely we ought to have heard something of them by now ? The boys have been out searching the country between here and the Nations and they haven't seen any sign of the rustlers or of the buggy. All tracks petered out after that wind the other night. The dust filled every hoof print and wheel track on the trails."

"There's a lot of wild country up there, George," Mary Ulrick commented wisely. "It would take a month to search *every* trail and track—and you know it just as well as I do. You can't do anything until the posse comes back anyway. The few fit men we've got on the ranch would be useless against the rustlers in that country. They'd be ambushed the moment they set foot in the Nations. Besides—you promised Mr. Earp you wouldn't do anything without consulting the Federal Marshal."

"I know, Mary. And I wish I hadn't made that promise now. What's the good of a Federal Marshal who lets thirty outlaws ride clean through his posse in the night, and then goes haring off in the opposite direction? The man's a fool—there are no two ways about it!"

Mary Ulrick held her tongue after this final outburst. She had more sense than to reason further with her husband when he was in this mood. Some intuition or sixth sense told her that Wyatt Earp would win through, she had been very impressed by his quiet confidence. He was no gun-wearing braggart—of that she was sure.

But George Ulrick had waited long enough. On the morning of the fourth day, with still no news of Wyatt Earp's whereabouts, he took matters into his own hands.

"I want volunteers to ride with me," he told his men as they ate breakfast in the bunk-house.

"What are you aimin' to do, boss?" Tom asked.

"First, try to link up with the marshal's posse, and join him in a full-scale hunt for the cattle. If we can't contact them within twenty-four hours there's only one thing for it. We'll have to go into the Nations ourselves and fight it out with hot lead."

"Now you're talkin' boss!" one of the hands called, and his fellow punchers joined in a chorus of approval of the rancher's words.

"You can't all go," George Ulrick warned them. "Tom, you aren't fit for the saddle yet, and I want you to stay behind and look after my wife and son. Grab a gun, and don't leave the house in any circumstances. Understand?"

"Yes, boss. I guess you're right," Tom acknowledged sadly. "I'll take good care o' them. You can depend on that."

One other man had to be left behind to care for the wounded men in the bunkhouse, but the others wasted no time in getting their horses and weapons ready for the sortie. Within twenty minutes they were assembled in front of the barn and George Ulrick hurried to join them from the ranch-house.

They travelled fast, the rancher's black horse setting a scorching pace, and soon they were out of the river pastures and heading due south on the trail the posse had taken. High up into the scrub-covered slopes they rode, spreading out as they raced southwards, and pausing only for brief moments at every ridge and hillock that gave them a view of the terrain ahead.

They sighted the posse sooner than they expected, coming upon them as they swung round a bluff a bare twenty miles from the Crown Bar. They rode wearily, worn out after more than a week of hard riding, their clothes thick with trail dust, and their horses driven to the point of exhaustion.

" We've drawn blank everywhere we've been," the Federal Marshal told George Ulrick as they met. " What brings you out in force ? "

In brief, curt sentences the rancher outlined the happenings of the past few days, but his news did little to penetrate the atmosphere of utter dejection that hung over the Marshal and his posse.

" I guess you can say good-bye to your cattle, Ulrick," the lawman told him. " By now they'll be either corralled for the winter up in the Nations or driven clear through to the railhead at Ellsworth an' sold along with a few thousand

Texan steers. No one's goin' to worry their heads over brand marks when the trains are loading for the east."

For a moment George Ulrick was speechless. "D'you mean to say you're giving up now?" he blazed angrily when he could control his voice.

"That's just what I do aim to do," the Marshal told him flatly. "My men are worn out, our horses are lame, an' there's no sense in carryin' on."

"But what about Earp and Burns?"

The Marshal shrugged his shoulders. "You should never have let them go, Ulrick. I'm not takin' my men out on a wild-goose chase after a couple of crazy fools in a buggy. They're dead men by now, that's a sure thing. The second posse has headed back for Witchita already, an' I aim to follow just as soon as the horses are fit, or we can get remounts."

But there were other men of sterner fibre in the posse. Although nearly asleep in their saddles with fatigue, they volunteered to join the rancher and his men in a last attempt at tracing the rustlers.

"If you can provide fresh horses, an' give us a chance to rest up for twelve hours, we'll ride with you—Marshal or no Marshal," they offered, and with this George Ulrick had to be content. Faced with the scorn of his own men, the

Marshal grudgingly agreed to accompany them, and the whole party joined forces for the return to the Crown Bar.

George Ulrick and his men fumed with impatience at the delay. To men eager for action there was nothing worse than being forced to match their speed to that of the lamed horses. When they were half-way to their home range the rancher sent two men ahead to warn his wife of their unexpected guests, and to arrange food and drink for the thirty-five-odd men in the combined party, but the day was well advanced as they rode down to the river pastures and made for the welcome of the ranch-house.

" I can almost smell the steaks cookin' from here," one of the men chortled as he sniffed the air hungrily.

" It won't be long now," George Ulrick grunted. " Once we're through the trees we're only a stone's throw from the home pasture."

But the sight that greeted them as they cleared the trees brought the whole party to a sudden halt.

Thirty horsemen ringed the ranch-house—their eyes fixed on the frail figure of Mary Ulrick as she protested angrily to two men who stood in the shadows of the ranch-house porch.

CHAPTER EIGHT

CHEROKEE TALKS

THE weary Marshal straightened up in his saddle as he took in the situation.

" Quick, men ! " he called excitedly. " Spread out, draw your guns, an' circle those men. We've got 'em corralled this time ! "

The riders obeyed swiftly, spurring their horses for a further burst of energy as they sped towards the ranch-house with the Marshal and George Ulrick in the lead.

The sound of their galloping horses reached the men clustered in the yard. They twisted round in their saddles and yelled wild warnings as their horses sidestepped and reared in jumbled confusion.

George Ulrick saw his wife step forward, shouting something he couldn't catch above the noise of the drumming hooves—and then she had jumped down from the porch and was running through the milling horsemen and out into the open.

" Don't shoot ! Don't shoot ! " she called as she ran straight towards them.

" Hold your fire ! " the Marshal roared at the

top of his voice, and then, as the gap between his posse and the running woman narrowed, he stood straight up in his stirrup irons, his rifle held high above his head in signal for a halt.

George Ulrick sprang from his saddle and ran to meet his wife with his six-gun still held ready in his hand.

" It's all right, George ! " Mary gasped as he reached her. " Mr. Earp's safe—and Jack Burns too. Those men aren't armed."

It was only then that George Ulrick raised his eyes and saw a familiar figure striding towards him.

" Jack ! " he exclaimed. " What in tarnation's goin' on ? "

Jack Burns's face was split by a grin that reached from ear to ear.

" Dismount your men, Marshal," he called as he approached. " There's no danger. Wyatt Earp's got the whole situation under control."

" What *is* happening ? Has everyone gone crazy ? " the Marshal blustered, swinging down from his horse. " Who are all these men ? "

" They *were* rustlers," the Crown Bar foreman grinned, " but they ain't any more—we talked 'em out of it. Wyatt will explain in a minute." He turned to his employer then with a merry twinkle in his eye : " Take a look down at the river bank, boss," he suggested. " There's

a mighty thirsty bunch o' Longhorns drinkin'
their fill at this very moment—sixteen hundred
of 'em ! "

The rancher could scarecly believe his eyes
as he followed the line of his foreman's pointing
arm, and saw the stolen cattle back on their
home range.

" How did you do it ? " he burst out.

Mary Ulrick answered. " You must ask Mr.
Earp that," she smiled. " We shall never be
able to thank him and Jack here enough for what
they have done. Come and see him now,
George—he's keeping an eye on the outlaws."

By now the entire posse had dismounted and
were clustered round them, trying to get an idea
of what was happening. They followed close
at the heels of the rancher and his wife, the
Marshal shaking his head in bewilderment.

Wyatt Earp stood at the ranch-house door,
leaning idly against the upright of the porch.
Tucked casually under his arm was his shortened
shotgun.

" How did you do it, Wyatt ? " George Ulrick
stammered, but the smiling man in the tail coat
brushed aside his questions.

" I'll tell you all about it later, George," he
told him. " Anderson and McMurray are tied
up in your parlour—you'd best hand them over to
the Marshal here, while I get rid of the rest of
the gang."

" Get rid of them ? What do you mean ? "

" Release them," Wyatt answered calmly.
" They were just leaving when you arrived."

The Marshal stepped forward. " Release
them ? " he repeated incredulously. " These
men are cattle thieves. I must take them back
to Witchita to stand trial."

Wyatt Earp's smile left his face.

" I said I was releasing them, Marshal," he
repeated quietly, and yet so distinctly that every
man could hear him. " I made a deal with
these men. They rode herd on George Ulrick's
steers for me all the way from the Wewoka
Valley. I gave my word that they would go
free when they had completed their bargain.
What's more they will leave here unharmed
by you or anyone else. They have my word
on it."

" What crazy nonsense is this ? " the Marshal
exploded. " I am arresting these men and taking
them to Witchita." He turned to his posse.
" Bring those men here with their hands tied
behind 'em," he ordered.

But even as they moved to obey, Wyatt Earp
stepped forward.

" Stand back ! " he ordered, his gun still
hanging idly in his arms, but a wealth of menace
in his voice. " My word is my bond, whether
it's given to a rustler or the President of the
United States. If any of you think differently

you'll have to settle with me—here and now."
He turned slowly to the Marshal. " And that
goes for you too, my friend," he said icily.

Under the silent menace of Wyatt Earp's shotgun the Marshal backed down. " I guess they're
your prisoners," he said lamely.

Wyatt nodded but he didn't answer. Instead he
walked easily to the nervous rustlers and told
them to ride.

" You've drawn your pay—now vamoose,"
he ordered. " And if I ever come across you in
any cattle-thievin' antics again, I'll join every
posse that hunts you down. Remember that
whenever you're tempted."

" I guess you would too, Mister," one of the
rustlers acknowledged, as he hastily led the way
through the posse and out into the gathering
twilight in safety.

Every man watched the outlaws ride away,
until they dipped out of sight beyond the river.

" You're welcome to go after 'em now, Marshal," Wyatt Earp stated as the last rider disappeared from view.

" With winded horses ? " the lawman muttered
angrily. " I don't know what your name is,
stranger, but when I do learn it I'll never forget
it as long as I live."

" The name's Earp. Wyatt Earp. What do
they call you, Marshal ? "

" Johnny Behan."

" Then keep out of my hair in future and I'll keep out of yours, Behan. You ought to be happy—you've got Anderson and McMurray to show for your trouble, and George Ulrick has retrieved his cattle. The Law should be well satisfied."

" You've made an enemy of that Marshal, Wyatt," George Ulrick stated grimly as he and Jack Burns joined Wyatt Earp at the breakfast table next morning. " He's an ugly man to cross."

But Wyatt only shrugged his shoulders.

" That's his worry," he said with a grin. " Without their leaders those hired hands of the rustlers were no danger to anyone. Running them in would only cause the State unnecessary expense at a time when the jails are overcrowded as it is. Surely even Behan has sense to see that ? "

" I'm just warning you," the rancher answered. " Johnny Behan is as vain as a peacock, and he'll never forget how you showed him up in front of his men. But don't let's worry our heads about that now. What we want to know is what you intend doing from now on ? Mary and I would be happy to have you stay with us for as long as you like. What do you say ? "

" No, George. I appreciate the offer, but I can't leave Cherokee to the tender mercies of Doc. Samuels any longer. I must ride over and see how he's getting on. With any luck his leg should have healed by now."

" Bring him back here," the rancher suggested. " Mary will soon feed the old rascal up and get him fit again."

But Wyatt Earp would not commit himself to any plans until he had seen his partner, and a few hours later he rode off from the Crown Bar with the good wishes of the entire outfit ringing in his ears.

" Come back soon," came Jack Burns's voice from the distance as he rode towards the river crossing, but something told Wyatt that he wouldn't be coming back, and that this was the last he would see of any of the Crown Bar folk.

He had been feeling unsettled all morning. Basically he wanted nothing better than to learn about cattle from just such an experienced rancher as George Ulrick, but whenever he tried to enter the trade all manner of events thwarted him. It seemed that he couldn't escape from becoming involved with the maintainence of law and order.

Maybe it was the influence of his lawyer father and his upbringing in a family that reverenced justice above all things ; or maybe it was the thrill of sudden action, and the knowledge that he was the equal of any man he had met as far as gunplay and cool courage were concerned.

The more Wyatt thought about it the less sure he was of his reasons. All he knew was that in some strange way his future seemed linked with the law. There was a challenge and a thrill in matching his brains against such men as Ben Thompson and the rustlers, such as he had not experienced in any other job he had tackled. At the same time he felt it his duty to uphold the law—without which the whole American civilisation would fold up.

These thoughts, and many others, filled Wyatt Earp's mind as he rode—and the more he thought, the more unsettled and restless he became.

It was in this mood that he reached Doc. Samuels's land, and caught sight of the Doctor himself riding to meet him astride a beautiful sorrel mare. Of Cherokee there was no sign.

" How is he, Doc ? " Wyatt asked anxiously of the wizened little man.

" Pretty fair, son. Pretty fair. He's as near fit as he'll ever be."

The words sent a feeling of apprehension over the younger man. " What exactly do you mean by that, Doc ? " he asked.

The little horse-doctor eyed him solemnly for a long while before he answered. When he did his words came as a shock to Wyatt.

" He'll never be able to stand any great strain on that leg again. The bone is damaged beyond repair."

For a moment Wyatt Earp was lost for words. The thought of old Cherokee, who had ridden and hunted and chased all over the West with him, being unable to carry on the active life that he was used to was almost too much to take in so suddenly.

" D'you mean he'll be a cripple, Doc ? " he gasped.

Doc. Samuels hastened to reassure him. " No, nothing of the kind, Mr. Earp ! It's just that he must take life easy from now on. No riding long distances, no cattle drovin' or walkin' any great distance. Apart from things like that he'll probably not even notice any handicap, son."

" Does he know this ? "

" No, son. I haven't told him. He's a cantankerous patient, as you can imagine, and I thought it best to leave you to tell him. I knew you'd be back as soon as you could."

Wyatt nodded unhappily. It was an unpleasant task, but he felt in his innermost heart that the little horse-doctor was right in his reasoning. " You're quite sure, Doc ? " he queried— knowing the answer as he uttered the words.

" Certain," the old man told him sadly.

" Then I guess the sooner he knows the better," said Wyatt with a deep sight, adding apologetically, " I guess it would be better if

I told him in my own way—alone—if you don't mind."

" Of course, my boy. I understand. You'll find him in the cabin."

" Thanks, Doc."

Wyatt Earp eased his horse forward, and made for the corral in front of the barn. He dismounted, untied the single cinch and slung the saddle across the top rail of the fence before turning the tired horse out to graze.

" Feed well, feller," he called softly as the gelding danced away happily. " You've earned it."

He turned then, and began the steep climb up to the cabin, his steps slowing as he neared the top. He hated the task that lay ahead of him, and for two pins he would've turned tail and cried off the ordeal, but he forced himself to continue. As he reached the ledge he looked up to find Cherokee regarding him thoughtfully from the doorway.

" You took your time," the old hunter grinned. " What's the matter—corns ? "

Wyatt smiled. " Tired," he replied. " Things have been a little hectic since we left you. I'll tell you all about it later. Right now I want to know how *you* are. I saw Doc. Samuel down the trail. He tells me your leg's healed well."

" What else did he tell you ? " Cherokee demanded unexpectedly.

" Nothing," Wyatt lied.

" You never could tell a lie without givin' yourself away," Cherokee informed him. " That's the trouble with you honest people—you make bad liars. Doc. is just the same."

" Then you know all about it, Cherokee ? " Wyatt asked, taking a seat on a tree stump and pushing his black stetson to the back of his head.

Cherokee Watson chuckled to himself as he too sat down. " Of course I know," he continued. " That old fool gave it away every time he checked over my leg. He hummed and hawed, an' carried on like an old hen with a clutch o' chicks to look after. I don't know the details, but I do know I shan't be a lot of use in the saddle. How bad is it, Wyatt ? Tell me straight out. I don't want to be kept guessin' any longer."

In simple, abrupt sentences Wyatt Earp told Cherokee what he had learned from Doc. Samuels only a little while before. The old man listened in silence, and when he looked up at his friend and partner there was a certain sadness in his eyes.

" I reckon you'll have to find another partner, Wyatt," was his only comment. " I'll be more hindrance than help to you if you're still keen on ranchin' for a livin'."

Wyatt Earp sprang to his feet. " Don't talk such nonsense ! " he protested angrily. " What

sort of partner do you take me for? To blazes
with the cattle trade, anyway. I've seen too much
of it already—the Texans and the rustlers between them are ruining the trade for Kansas cattle
men. There are other ways of making a living,
and there's no reason why you can't join me."

But Cherokee shook his head. "No, son," he
said deliberately. "A lot has happened to us
both in the past few months, whether you
realise it or not. I'm kinda glad this leg o'
mine has brought things to a head."

Wyatt's eyes widened at Cherokee's serious
tones. "What's in your mind?" he asked
quietly.

Cherokee was silent for a long time as he sought
the words with which to express what he felt.

"It's this way, Wyatt," he said at length.
"You don't need a pardner any more. You're
at your best when you have only yourself to
consider. You're a lone wolf now—and I've
got a notion where you're headed when you've
sorted out your thoughts a mite."

Wyatt realised with a start that Cherokee was
giving voice to all the puzzling thoughts that he
himself had been worrying over all the way
from the Crown Bar. He had always known
that the old hunter was no fool—but now his
respect had deepened beyond measure.

"Go on," he said.

"You're all mixed up, son," the old man

told him. " You don't know what you do want to do yet. You've tried your hand at most things, and I've strung along with you. It wasn't 'til you stepped out into the plaza at Ellsworth the other day that I woke up to what lies before you. It's a trade you're cut out for—and I'm not."

" What's that, Cherokee ? "

" The Law," Cherokee said emphatically.

" But I don't want to become just another hired gunman ! " Wyatt protested.

Cherokee leaned forward as though to add further weight to his next words. " No ! " he cried. " That's one thing you'll never be— *not just another hired gunman*. You're different from the rest o' the Marshals an' gunfighters. You don't like killin' ! "

Wyatt Earp was bewildered. His friend's words just didn't make sense to him.

" Sit down an' listen ! " Cherokee urged him, and to his surprise he obeyed without protest.

" Think back to Ellsworth," Cherokee counselled. " What happened there ? You walked right out and arrested Ben Thompson *without drawin' your gun*. Then you ordered him out of Town *without firing a shot to persuade him.* Then you drew on George Peshaur when he went for his gun—*but you didn't pull the trigger !* I don't know what's been happenin' up at George Ulrick's ranch, but I'll lay a bag o' beans to a silver dollar you haven't fired your gun unless there was no other way o' dealin' with the situation."

"I know all that," Wyatt broke in irritably. "But that's how things were. There wasn't any need to fire. What's all this leading up to?"

Cherokee smote the palm of his hand with a clenched fist. "Can't you see, son!" he roared. "*You're a natural born law-enforcer.* You know exactly how to handle a situation by some sort of instinct, an' then you go right out an' see it through. Men know it the minute they see you. They read it in your eyes. Like Ben Thompson, they know you'll beat them to the draw, an' they know they're licked afore they start. You'll be the greatest Marshal in the West one day—you mark my words."

And with that Cherokee got to his feet and stumped off into the cabin. When he returned Wyatt was still sitting on the tree stump, lost in thought.

"Come on, Wyatt," the old man grumbled. "Take this kit o' mine an' give me a hand to saddle the horses. We're ridin' straight away."

"Where to?" Wyatt Earp asked in amazement.

"Witchita. They're holdin' the elections an' Mayor Jim Holt's lookin' for a Marshal to take over the Town if he's elected."

CHAPTER NINE

WITCHITA

AT FIRST sight Witchita appeared to be just another cattle town. It sprawled and straggled along the bank of the Arkansas River in typical Western fashion—an untidy jumble of wood and corrugated iron.

But Witchita was, on closer inspection, a town with a future. Thanks to its toll bridge over the river, which separated the business and residential quarters from the cattle camps at Cowskin Creek, Witchita was building up a big population of permanent settlers, storekeepers and traders. Construction of houses from brick and stone was fast replacing the earlier turf and wood building ; it boasted a wide main thoroughfare, intersecting side streets, and three-storied houses ; and above all it had more stores, more saloons, and more gambling halls than any of its neighbours.

Witchita was booming. It already had a population of over twelve hundred people, and on the prairies to the south and west of the town a further two thousand Texan cowboys rode herd on more than two hundred thousand Long-horn steers as they grazed and fattened until the trains arrived to take them to market. Witchita was bigger, busier, noisier—and wilder than Ellsworth ever could be.

" Quite a place ! " Cherokee grunted. " There'll be more than enough work for a dozen marshals by the looks o'things. Let's go find Jim Holt an' see if he's got a job for you."

Wyatt Earp was doubtful of his chances. " He'll probably say I'm too young, Cherokee," he told his friend. " After all I'm well under thirty, and I've only held a badge for a day."

Cherokee snorted. " You didn't worry your head about that before. And I didn't hear any remarks about your age from Ben Thompson. You scared the livin' daylights outa him without much trouble. Come along, an' don't be so all-fired modest."

They halted their horses at a hitching rail in Main Street, tied them securely, and went in search of the Mayor's office on foot.

But when they ran him to earth, Mayor Holt was busy with Judge Jewett and refused to see them. " Come back later, son," one of the deputies told Wyatt. " If it's urgent leave your name and where you're stayin', an' he'll send word when he's free."

" The name's Earp, Wyatt Earp," the tall Illinoian informed him, " but I can't tell you where we'll be stayin', we've only ridden into town this morning."

At his words the deputy eyed him curiously.

" Where are you from, stranger ? " he asked.

Wyatt grinned. " All over," he said. " The last town we hit was Ellsworth."

The man started at the name. " Wait here a minute, Mr. Earp ! " he exclaimed. " I'll see the Mayor right away." And with that he bolted through a door and disappeared.

" What goes on ? " Wyatt queried, but Cherokee held his peace.

" Wait an' see, son," he chuckled.

They hadn't long to wait. A minute later the deputy returned. Behind him followed a thick-set man of middle age, clean shaven, clear of eye, and with a determined tilt to his chin. His gaze shifted rapidly from Wyatt Earp to Cherokee and back again.

" Which one of you's Wyatt Earp ? " he demanded in a deep voice.

" I am."

" Are you the man who ran Ben Thompson out of Ellsworth ? "

Wyatt nodded. " I guess so," he answered. " Leastways, he left town at my suggestion."

A smile broke over the Mayor's face. He held out his hand. " We've heard all about it, Earp," he grinned. " I'd like to shake hands with the man who did that to Thompson. He's been a pain in the neck to every law officer in the West. Witchita's still buzzin' with the news."

" Someone had to do something," Wyatt muttered with embarrassment. " But I didn't come here to discuss Ben Thompson. I want to see you about a job."

" What sort of a job ? "

" I hear you need a deputy marshal now you've been elected, Mr. Holt. Reckon I'd like to have a crack at a little trouble shooting if the job's still vacant."

Mayor Holt didn't hesitate. " Get yourself a gun, my friend," he smiled. " You're hired. Buy the best weapons you can find at the New York Store, charge them to me, and then come back here an' tell me how you beat Ben Thompson. We need men like you in Witchita."

" Got a job for me as well ? " Cherokee broke in.

The Mayor scratched his head. " Can you use a gun ? " he asked.

" Use a gun ? " Cherokee spluttered indignantly. " Why man, I taught this boy here all he knows—me an' Wild Bill Hickok that is."

Wyatt caught the Mayor's eye and winked one eye deliberately. " That's correct, Mr. Holt," he said seriously. " Cherokee taught me how to load a gun an' Wild Bill taught me how to use one."

The Mayor roared with laughter. " Seems like you two understand one another pretty well," he chuckled. " It'd be a pity to separate you."

He turned to Cherokee. " We need a jailer," he went on. " How would that suit you ? "

" I'm your man ! " Cherokee accepted. " Let young Wyatt fill the cells an' I'll see they stay full. What's the pay ? "

" We'll talk about that later, when you've got your guns," the Mayor answered.

" Suits me," the old hunter said as he led the way out into the street.

Half an hour later Wyatt Earp was sworn in as deputy marshal of Witchita and found himself in the Mayor's private office listening to a tale of woe.

" This town's runnin' wild," Jim Holt told him. " The Texan cowhands are out of our control. It's become a point of pride with them to hurrah the town every time they ride in. They wear guns openly against all local ordinances, they terrorise the womenfolk, an' there isn't a day goes by without a shooting, a dozen fist-fights or a heap o' senseless damage. We've just got to do somethin' about it before they drive the law-abiding citizens away from Witchita for good. Several families have left already an' more are packin' at this very minute. I'll give you a free hand, and back you all the way if you can knock a bit of sense into these madmen."

" I'll try," Wyatt agreed, " but I'm not promising anything until I get the feel of the town. Where's your main trouble spot ? "

The Mayor shrugged and opened his hands expressively. " Anywhere," he answered. " The Texans aren't much worried where they start a fight. The two worst places are the Keno House on Douglas Avenue, and Rowdy Kate's across the toll-bridge. You'll find trouble enough inside or outside both those places any time you like."

Wyatt got to his feet. " Then I guess I'd better start right away," he said grimly.

A gesture from the Mayor stopped him as he moved for the door. " There's just one thing you ought to know, Wyatt," he warned his new marshal.

" What's that ? "

" Ben Thompson's in town—and so's George Peshaur. Don't take any chances—they'll be gunnin' for you the moment they hear you're in Witchita."

" That's their worry," the young marshal grunted as he walked out into Main Street.

News travelled fast in Witchita.

" Jim Holt's appointed a new marshal," one lounger told another after he had heard Wyatt tell the storekeeper to charge his guns to the Mayor.

" What's his name ? "

" Earp. Wyatt Earp."

" Never heard of him."

" Nor have I—but I guess we'd better tell the boys. They'll enjoy a little marshal baitin' for a change." And without more ado the two idlers ambled over to the Occidental and spread the tidings.

To their surprise the new marshal's name caused a sudden silence at the bar of the saloon.

" Earp ? Why that's the man who stood up to Ben Thompson in Ellsworth ! " a cowboy exclaimed. " Holy smoke ! This is really somethin' to tell the gang at Cowskin Creek." And he raced out of the saloon, grabbed his horse and headed out across the toll bridge to the cattle camps.

" Guess we'd better warn Ben," another cowhand muttered, and he too disappeared hastily.

Within half an hour the whole town, from the Judge to the meanest washer-up in the Southern had heard the news, and Ben Thompson, dealing cards in the Keno House, issued his warning.

" Stay clear o' that feller," he counselled. " He's poison—an' what's more he's not afraid of any livin' man."

But the Texans were not convinced. They sought out George Peshaur and asked his opinion.

" Wyatt Earp ? He was just lucky at Ellsworth. You wait an' see. I'll show you how to tame Mr. Wyatt Earp once an' for all. I'll get that feller as sure as my name's Peshaur. Stick around, boys, there'll be some fun to-night."

One of the first to hear Peshaur's boast was Cherokee Watson. He had slipped into the New York Store to buy some new clothes in place of his ancient trail-stained buckskins. The dignity of his new post had already driven him to consult a mirror, and the sight of his untrimmed moustache, and the grey hair that curled down the back of his neck until it nearly reached his shoulders, had persuaded him that it was about time he smartened up. His first call had been at a barber's, where the long-suffering owner made short work of his luxuriant growth of hair and bristle.

"Gee! I'll have to charge you double, Mister," the barber grumbled, when he saw the magnitude of his task. "I've been cuttin' for a full five minutes and I ain't found your ears yet."

"Pah!" the old hunter snorted. "You youngsters don't recognise a good head o' hair when you see one. This ain't nothin'. You wait 'til I grow my winter pelt—this is only a summer thatch. An' don't you cut too much off, you thievin' varmint," he added angrily as he saw in the mirror the slaughter that was going on behind his back. "I'll come for you with a gun in my hand if I catch my death of cold."

But the barber's handiwork had already whittled down his curls to such an extent that Cherokee was forced to buy a new hat.

" An' what's the use of a new hat," the old man groused to the assistant who served him at the New York Store. " You can't drink out of it, 'cos the die comes out, and it ain't any good for keeping the rain out 'til it's got a good layer o' grease on it."

" But a man in your position must have smart clothes," the assistant advised him, with his tongue in his cheek. " A jailer must impress the Mayor, and the Judge, and the deputies—and the prisoners. What you need is a whole new outfit, otherwise you'll find you'll get mistaken for a vagrant, and end up in your own cells."

Cherokee eyed the youngster suspiciously. " D'you reckon so ? " he queried at length.

" I certainly do, Mister," came the reply. " Just you try this outfit I've got here. It's just the thing for a jailer, and it's cheap at forty dollars."

" Forty dollars ! " the old man cried. " Man, I can buy two prime four-year steers for that ! " But he bought the suit, *and* a hat, *and* a pair of flat-heeled boots before he left the store.

He was waiting for his change when two other customers fell to discussing the appointment of Wyatt Earp to the vacant law-enforcement post. He cocked an ear and listened intently.

" Don't give much for his chances," one of the men was saying.

" How come ? "

" The Texans have got it in for him already. That no-good Peshaur is out to tame him, so I hear. It should be worth watching."

The second man nodded. " He's an ugly fighter, sure enough," he agreed. " I'd lay a hundred dollars he'll drill this Earp feller the moment he goes for his gun—but I don't figure anyone would take my bet."

" I wouldn't, that's a sure thing," laughed his friend.

Cherokee strode across the store. " I'll take that bet, Mister," he said quietly. " Let's see the colour o' your money and I'll match it in gold. Wyatt Earp'll cut that Peshaur character down to size in seconds."

" I hate to take your money, stranger," said the man as he counted out the coins and slammed them on the counter. " I know Peshaur."

" And I know Wyatt Earp," grinned Cherokee.

CHAPTER TEN

TWO-FISTED LAW

DESPITE the wager he had just made, Cherokee was very worried as he stepped out into Douglas Avenue and turned into Main Street.

" I *must* find Wyatt and warn him," he muttered to himself, as he hurried in the direction of the Mayor's office as fast as his stiff leg would allow him.

There was an atmosphere of suspense in the air, as though the whole town held its breath as it awaited the threatened gunfight. The streets were packed with townsfolk and cowboys, the saloons were doing a roaring trade in rot-gut whisky, rye, and corn liquor, and every minute saw fresh arrivals cross the tollbridge from Cowskin Creek.

Of Wyatt there was no sign. Cherokee reached the office, flung open the door and found himself face to face with the Mayor.

" Where's Wyatt ? " the old man demanded.

" Out on patrol. Why, what's happened ? "

" Nothin'—yet," Cherokee answered. " But things'll be poppin' pretty soon. Peshaur's gunnin' for Wyatt. The whole town's talkin' about it."

The Mayor frowned. " I warned him before he left," he said. " But I didn't expect it to start as soon as this. Grab a six-gun and come with me—he may need help."

" A shotgun would be better. Peshaur ain't the kind to make a move without half a hundred cowhands behind him," Cherokee commented, taking a riot gun from the rack and loading rapidly.

Out in the street there was still no sign of Wyatt Earp, but the sound of George Peshaur's voice, raised high in boasting talk of what he would do to the marshal when they met, came floating across to them from the sidewalk of the Keno House.

They hurried forward and were just in time to see Wyatt Earp appear on the fringe of the crowd of excited cowboys. Cherokee's mouth dropped open, and Mayor Holt exclaimed in surprise, for as the marshal strolled unconcernedly towards Peshaur, and the Texans edged back out of the line of fire, they saw him unbuckle his gunbelt !

" What in thunder does he think he's doing ? " cried the Mayor.

" Search me ! " Cherokee sighed. " But whatever it is that boy's got somethin' up his sleeve."

" I surely hope so—otherwise he'll be a dead man in minutes."

But Wyatt's agile mind had already solved the problem of how to tame George Peshaur once and for all. He knew in his bones that the happenings of the next few minutes were critical as far as his future as a marshal was concerned. He had got to slam this braggart Texan hard and in a way that would wound the pride of every cowboy and cattleman who backed him. And that was just what he was about to do.

" Peshaur," he called as he handed his guns to a bystander without pausing in his stride. " You talk big with a gun in your hand. Let's see how you fight without one."

Peshaur stepped forward. " What d'you mean, Earp ? " he asked.

" What I say. Take off your guns and I'll teach you the lesson you've been needing far too long. Come on, man ! I'm going to show you up for what you are—a bluffer, a bully, and a coward."

For a second there wasn't a man who didn't expect the Texan to snatch his gun and drop the marshal in his tracks. His hand moved down to his holster, but instead of grasping the butt of his six-gun, it flew to the buckle, undid the strap, and with an oath Peshaur flung his guns into the dust of the street. An evil grin of expectation settled on his face as he stood towering above the six-foot Illinoian—a full four inches taller, fifty pounds heavier, and with a reputation as a fist fighter that was the pride of every Texan trail herder.

" I hope you know what you're doin', sonny," he sneered. " Where do we fight—here in the street or in private ? "

" In private," Wyatt answered. He turned to the crowd. " Is there an empty room handy ? " he demanded.

A storekeeper answered. " Right behind you, marshal. Help yourself, and I'll gladly stand the bill for any damage."

" Right. Come on, Peshaur. Let's see what you're made of," Wyatt called as he led the way to the back room.

Mayor Holt and Cherokee dived into the crowd, fighting their way to the door of the store.

" Get back an' stay back," the hunter roared at the Texans who moved to follow their champion. " They'll fight this out alone, an' you can pick up Peshaur when the marshal's finished with him."

But Cherokee's heart had sunk into his new boots on hearing Wyatt's challenge. Try as he would, Wyatt didn't stand a chance against the bull-like cowboy, and Cherokee knew it. What had ever possessed him to issue the challenge was beyond him. A gunfight, yes, for with Wyatt's speed there was little doubt of the outcome—as long as Peshaur's friends didn't join in. But a fistfight with that great hulking bully was an entirely different matter.

With a feeling of utter helplessness Cherokee heard the key turn in the lock behind him, and silence descended upon the expectant crowd.

For a full fifteen minutes the walls of the wooden building shook to the crash of falling bodies as the two men hurled themselves at each other. The very foundations quivered, and the door splintered, sagging drunkenly on its hinges. The crowd could scarcely contain itself in its excitement. Gamblers among them who thronged the street cried offers of wagers at fantastic odds—but there were no takers. Even Cherokee held his peace—even when one man offered him one hundred dollars to one that Peshaur would win. He wasn't prepared to throw one single dollar away on Wyatt's chances. He just didn't have a hope—and there was nothing he could do about it.

As the noise from inside the locked room reached a crescendo Cherokee could stand it no longer. He moved towards the door, only to find Mayor Holt's gun in his ribs.

" Leave 'em alone, my friend," the Mayor ordered, and Cherokee moved weakly back to his post at the front of the building.

As he reached the sidewalk all noise from the room ceased suddenly. Every voice died, and all eyes stared at the splintered door.

They heard the key turn slowly in the lock. The door creaked open—and there, swaying slightly on his feet on the threshold, stood the battered figure of the marshal !

Wyatt's shirt was in ribbons, his lips were split and his knuckles raw. He stared back at them, his eyes empty of all expression, and then he walked shakily to the street door.

No one spoke a word as the marshal picked up his hat, re-fixed his badge, and shook the long black hair out of his eyes. He reached for the gunbelt that was handed to him, strapped it slowly into place, then took a long keen look at the Texans who stood with gaping mouths below him.

" Get him out of there," he ordered, and with that he settled his hat on his head and walked off into Main Street.

Years later the beating of George Peshaur by the young marshal was hailed as the greatest single episode in his career as a deputy marshal in Witchita. It had been a case of calm scientific fist-fighting against brute force, and the Texan bully bore the scars of his defeat ever afterwards.

For days the fight was the talk of Cowskin Creek, and the cowboys camped along its banks eyed the tall figure of Jim Holt's new deputy with an awakened respect as he patrolled the streets of Witchita.

But Wyatt Earp was not one to bask in personal glory, however well earned. With the skill and insight of a campaigning general he sensed the full importance of his victory.

" Now's our chance, Mr. Holt," he urged the Mayor as he brushed aside the congratulations that were showered upon him by his fellow deputies. " We've got to follow up with all the strength we can muster. Get all your marshals out in force. We'll clean this town up before the Texans are awake to what's happened."

" How d'you mean, Wyatt ? " Jim Holt asked. " I'll do anything you suggest if it's going to keep the peace in this township."

" Give orders to every man on your payroll to arrest on sight for wearing a gun within the town limits. Tell the Judge what you propose and tell him to stand by for daily court sessions. It's our biggest chance yet to tame these cow-hands."

Judge Jewett welcomed the proposal. " Go ahead," he chuckled. " Keep them in jail over-night and I'll fine 'em all one hundred dollars in the morning—rich and poor alike."

By nightfall the heavily increased force of deputy marshals, working in pairs to lessen the temptation to resist arrest, had over twenty would-be trouble-makers safely under lock and key. An hour later another ten had been brought in, and Cherokee Watson was at his wits' end to find accommodation for them in the already crowded jail.

" I thought you said this was an easy job, Mayor," he grumbled to Jim Holt. " I've been hoppin' about like a flea in a blanket since noon. The jail's fair bustin' at the seams with these gentlemen from the Lone Star State. An' the things they're callin' Wyatt," he added with a grin, " why, you'd think he was the very Devil himself to hear them talk."

But despite Cherokee's protests at the extra work the wholesale jailing of all offenders against the " no-guns " order continued unabated for the best part of a week, and the Judge, rubbing his hands with glee, relieved them all of one hundred dollars, and warned them that the next offence would result in the doubling of the fine, and the confiscation of their guns for good.

Miraculously the attitude of the cowboys changed. Guns were an expensive item of every-day necessity. Without them a man could neither work stampeding Longhorns, nor defend himself and his cattle from attack. Coupled with a two-hundred-dollar fine, the threat of confiscation was a powerful deterrent.

A week later peace had descended upon Witchita, a peace broken only by an occasional brawl that was quickly quashed by the marshals. But it was an uneasy peace, achieved by threats and harsh handling of all law-breakers, and Jim

Holt and Wyatt Earp had no illusions about its temporary nature.

Threats of retaliation were already drifting in to the Mayor's office via friendly cattlemen and keen-eared storekeepers. There were whispers of a mass attack on the law officers by a hundred armed Texans, and Wyatt Earp's name figured high in every scrap of fighting talk that came to them.

"Watch your step, Wyatt, you're a marked man," Jim Holt warned his new deputy.

"I'm ready for them," Wyatt answered. "Just warn the boys to let me handle things in my own way. When trouble breaks they must hold their fire until I let loose. If they don't this town will have a pitched battle on its hands and a full graveyard." He looked earnestly into the Mayor's eyes as he spoke. "I mean it, Mr. Holt," he repeated. "No firing until I start, or a score of innocent bystanders may well die."

Jim Holt nodded. "I guess you know what you're doing," he said.

"I do. And I've made my preparations. There are a dozen loaded scatter-guns placed all over town, in stores, behind house doors, and under sidewalk boards. Wherever trouble starts I'll have a riot-gun within reach. They may get me—but I'll wing a round dozen before they do."

By now every law officer and temporary deputy on the Mayor's payroll was warned to hold himself in readiness, while down on Cowskin Creek the Texans laid their plans and cleaned their guns expectantly.

But without a leader to unite them, the cowboys fell to arguing among themselves, and soon a dozen different plans were having an airing round the chuck-wagons and the nightly camp fires out on the prairie. George Peshaur was no longer capable of taking part; Ben Thompson still stuck to his refusal to be mixed up in any attack upon Wyatt Earp; and the wealthiest cattle man of them all—Shanghai Pierce—was languishing in jail for his part in a brawl in Witchita's Main Street.

And so the uneasy peace continued, with daily threats on one side, and constant vigilance and preparedness on the other, until news of a large herd of Longhorns approaching from the south-west came to the town.

First estimates of the herd ranged between two and four thousand head, but when eventually the point riders led the way up towards the waters of the Arkansas it became apparent that this was one of the biggest herds to be brought up from Texas during the whole season. A full six thousand steers were soon tearing hungrily at the lush grass of the river pastures or wallowing belly-deep in the mud of the watering places, and with them came a hundred mounted cowhands to swell the ranks of the discontents across the toll bridge from the town of Witchita. At their head rode Mannen Clements.

" Mannen Clements ! " cried Jim Holt when the news was brought to him as he ate breakfast with Wyatt and Cherokee. " Now things'll come to a head. That man's caused more trouble than any ten ranchers put together."

Wyatt looked up from his plate with interest. " Tell me about him," he urged.

Jim Holt sighed deeply. " It'd take all day to detail his crimes. His boast is that he has hurrahed every cattle town between here and Dallas. He even paints the name of each town and law officer he has beaten up across the canvas of his chuck-wagon. He's driven four marshals out of Hays and Abilene already."

" What's he like with a gun ? " asked Cherokee with a worried frown.

Jim Holt's reply was short and to the point. " Fast and deadly. He's a boaster—but he's no fool, and he hasn't met his match yet. There are fifteen killings chalked up against him to my knowledge."

" Then I guess we'd better be ready to welcome him to Witchita," said Wyatt grimly as he reached for his gunbelt and prepared to make his first patrol of the day.

CHAPTER ELEVEN

DAWN ATTACK

WITH the coming of Mannen Clements and his men Cowskin Creek began to seethe with excitement. Here at last was the one man who could lead the Texans in driving Wyatt Earp from Witchita, and smashing the new-found power of Mayor Holt and his law officers. Gone was the indecision of the past weeks—the time had come for action.

" So you've got a new marshal in Witchita who needs tamin'," grinned Mannen Clements when they told him of the happenings of the past few weeks. " I guess that's the best news I've heard in months. The boys are spoilin' for a little fun, and I reckon this little outin' is about our mark." He turned to his men with an ugly glint in his eyes. " What d'you say, boys ? D'you feel like takin' on this upstart marshal with guns in your hands ? "

A wild yell of delight greeted his words.

" Just lead us to him, Mannen ! " one man cried as he whipped out his six-guns and fired them high above his head in his exuberance.

" Right. That's settled then. This is what

we'll do . . ." And without waiting to hear more of Witchita and its problems Mannen Clements went right into the preparation of his plans to run Wyatt Earp " up a tree " next day.

Meanwhile the law officers hadn't been idle. Unknown to the ringleaders of the Texans they had friends among the cattlemen who had no wish to go against the town. Soon Mannen Clements's plan was common knowledge, and Wyatt Earp grinned quietly to himself as the reports came in.

" The only thing I don't know yet is the time they intend moving," he told the Mayor. " My guess is that it'll be early to-morrow, before the town's properly awake."

It was Cherokee Watson who accidentally discovered this vital information, and was able to complete the full picture for his friend and his fellow marshals. As he busied himelf about his duties in the crowded jail he chanced to hear a remark that confirmed Wyatt's opinion. It came from a new prisoner, who had only been arrested that afternoon for disturbing the peace by riding his horse along the sidewalk and into the town's leading saloon by the main door.

" We'll all be outa here by nine to-morrow," the man whispered to his companions through the bars. " Then we'll see who runs this town, by Gosh. Mannen's got fifty men hand-picked for his little jaunt, and he'll move so early he'll catch the marshals with their pants down."

Chuckling to himself Cherokee went in search of Wyatt. " No sleep for you to-night, my friend," he grinned when he found him. " You'll have to have your wits about you around dawn if what this feller says is true."

" Nice work, Cherokee ! " Wyatt smiled. " I was goin' to sleep out on the bench in front of Billy Collins's place anyway, in case things started that early. But now I'll see the boys are out there with me too."

As he relaxed on the hard wood of the bench that night, Wyatt fell to thinking over his new way of life, and the things that Cherokee had told him about himself when they were up in Doc. Samuels's cabin in the hills. To his surprise he found that he was looking forward to the testing time ahead—just as Cherokee had said he would. There was nothing very satisfying in upholding the Law against such riff-raff as he had faced of late, but to match his strength and skill against George Peshaur had given him a big kick. He smiled wryly to himself as he thought of what went on behind the closed door of that little room. It had been quite a fight !

And now he was about to match his wits against an even more deadly menace. He tried to put himself in Mannen Clements's shoes, asking himself what he would do if he were the cowboy leader. Of one thing he was sure—Clements would swallow no bluff, and by all accounts he was no coward. The only thing he would respect would be strength. They must be ready to match him, man for man and gun for gun, and strike hard at the first move.

Long before the first faint streaks of light were showing in the eastern sky Wyatt stirred himself, stretching cat-like in the darkness. He got to his feet and felt his way towards his sleeping men.

" On your feet, friend," he murmured quietly as he shook the first deputy awake. " Grab your rifle and take up position in Douglas Avenue. That's where they'll come as soon as they've crossed the toll bridge."

Soon twelve yawning men were strung out across Douglas Avenue at the point where it met Main Street. Each man had a Winchester under his arm, a full belt of cartridges slung across his waist. Mannen Clements's reception committee was all set to greet him.

Wyatt saw his men into position and then moved forwards towards the toll bridge. He went fifty yards up Douglas Avenue, until he found a wide, iron-hooped water butt beside one of the stores. Here he halted—out of sight from watching eyes when the sun rose above the mountains.

Slowly the minutes dragged by without a sound from the toll-bridge.

Ten minutes. Fifteen minutes. Twenty. . . .

A movement right behind him brought Wyatt twirling fast—his gun flashing into his hand with his thumb crooked hard back over the hammer.

A stray cat jumped away from him, arching its back and spitting.

" Holy Mackerel ! " he sighed, as he put his gun back. " Puss, you surely frightened the life out of me ! "

But next minute he heard a warning sound from far ahead. This was no false alarm. It came again. The sound of a horseshoe ringing on the bolts that held the timbers of the bridge.

" Here they come," he called softly to his men. " Hold your fire and wait for me to move."

" Watch yourself, son," one of the deputies called back.

The light was flooding in fast now, red tinted and angry. It lit up the length of Douglas Avenue, glinting on the glass fronts of the saloons, and the windows of the houses and stores. All eyes focused warily upon the fifty riders who moved steadily towards the waiting lawmen over the bridge and into the dust of Witchita.

Wyatt crouched behind the water butt, his

eyes glued to the tall, dark man who rode at the head of the cowboys. Clements was wide-shouldered, narrow-hipped and athletic-looking. He rode stiffly, his back straight, and his boots thrust forward in the stirrups. A shapeless black hat sat carelessly on his dark hair and his over-wide spaced eyes were shaded by thick coarse brows.

Steadily the band of horsemen moved up Douglas Avenue, their mounts held back to a jogging trot as they scanned the sidewalks for sign of opposition. As they came they spread out, filling the street from side to side.

They were halfway up towards the Main Street junction when they spotted the line of waiting riflemen, and the sight brought them to an immediate halt. Mannen Clements squinted visibly as he eyed the levelled rifles. He turned in his saddle and muttered a brief order that Wyatt failed to catch, and straight away the cowboys swung down from their saddles and spread out on foot, taking cover behind corner posts and hitching rails as their leader handed his horse to the men detailed to watch the animals in the rear.

Wyatt still made no move. The attackers were closing rapidly now, guns drawn in readiness for the first shot to be fired, and he could hear their voices calling to one another.

" Where's this marshal feller—Earp, or what-

ever you call him ? " he heard Clements snarl to
one of his men.

" Can't see him, Mannen. It's odd. He's
not up there with the others."

And then Wyatt judged that the time had
come to make his play. He stepped out from
the cover of the water butt and walked casually
across the street towards the cowboy leader.

Clements stopped dead, his gun levelled at the
glint of the marshal's badge above Wyatt's
heart, but Wyatt paid no attention as he walked
steadily forward with twin guns still swinging,
low in his holsters—undrawn.

Still Clements held his fire. His Texan pride
forbade him from firing on any adversary without fair warning. If he did he would never be
able to claim that he had outgunned this upstart
marshal whose reputation was so high in Witchita.
He knew his men were watching every move he
made so that they could recount the famous
meeting of cowboy leader and marshal round
the camp fires on many a cattle drive in the
future. He knew it—and Wyatt knew it. He
had planned it that way.

Only thirty paces separated the two men when
Wyatt spoke.

" Put up your guns, Mannen," he ordered,
loud and clear in the silence of the lonely street.

Clements hesitated, at a loss to know what to
do.

" You heard, Mannen ! " Wyatt roared. " Put up those guns, and get back to camp."

For what seemed an age the two men faced each other, neither yielding, and behind them their respective followers awaited the outcome. Wyatt still moved slowly forward, his hands within easy reach of his guns, but making no move to draw them. His cold, grey eyes stared full at Clements's, willing him to obey, and the cowboy leader read death in their icy bleakness.

Suddenly, without a word, Clements turned on his heel, holstered his gun and gave the order to ride out of town.

As he stood in the centre of the street and watched the last of the horsemen canter over the bridge, Wyatt heard again Cherokee Watson's words.

" Can't you see, son," the old man's voice echoed in his head. " You're a natural born law-enforcer. You don't need to fire a shot— men look in your eyes and know they're beaten before they start. You'll be the greatest Marshal in the West one day."

And right then and there, in the streets of Witchita, Wyatt Earp knew that Cherokee was right.

CHAPTER TWELVE

CALL FROM DODGE

As WEEK followed week, and months came and went, more cattle flowed into the prairies to await their turn for shipment. Huge double-header freighting trains, with high smoke-stacks and steel-grill cow-catchers mounted before them, puffed in from the East, loaded the bawling steers in their thousands, and puffed out again to the cheers of the cowboys. Whole outfits of cowhands were paid off, and left to find their way back home to Texas as best they could, or to forsake cattle droving and head for the mines, or the buffalo grounds, or the lumber camps.

New herds meant new faces, and itchy trigger-fingers—but a single day in Witchita under the eagle eye of Wyatt Earp and his marshals, was enough to take the edge off any ideas the new-comers may have of hurrahing the township. Coupled with the news of Mannen Clements's defeat, and the beating of George Peshaur, the sight of Marshal Earp's prompt dealing with the slightest breach of the peace was good cause for forsaking gunplay for the duration of their stay around Witchita.

But there was always at least one fool in every outfit who got into his head that he was faster and slicker and more proficient with a gun than any marshal born. Without exception Wyatt Earp met all comers, disarmed them, and threw them into jail to cool off and learn some sense. Elections came, Mayor Holt retired from public office, and the new Mayor Mike Meagher made Wyatt his Town Marshal, with authority over all other law officers in Witchita.

"I give you a free hand, Wyatt," the new Mayor told him. "Keep the town as free from trouble as it is at present, and the job's yours for as long as you like. There's only one thing," he added a word of caution, "don't slacken up now. There are still a few men like George Peshaur who've got it in for you."

But Wyatt didn't need any warning. He had seen too many marshals who grew careless after their first successes. He had seen them driven from town at gunpoint when they least expected it, or buried deep in the graveyard on Boot Hill, and he had no intention of joining them.

Even so, he was making his nightly rounds of the saloons and gambling houses when a sudden challenge from behind fetched him to an instant halt. He turned slowly, to find a young cowboy facing him with a drawn gun in his hand.

"I'm goin' to kill you, marshal," the youngster

sneered. " You've had it comin' to you for a long time, an' I'm the feller to finish with you once an' for all. Reach for your gun an' I'll drop you."

For a second or two Wyatt didn't make a move, but when he did his hands flew so fast that spectators swore they never followed them. There was a roar from his Peacemaker, a flash of exploding cordite, and a scream of pain as the bullet smashed the braggart's gun hand.

" That'll teach you not to play with firearms, sonny," the marshal said with a grim smile as he hurled the eighteen-year-old into one of Cherokee's cells.

Cherokee helped to patch the wounded hand as best he could, his eyes puzzled and a deep frown etched across his brow.

" Why didn't you kill him, Wyatt ? " he asked at length.

Wyatt Earp looked surprised. " Why ? " he asked. " He'll never try a durned fool stunt like that again. I thought I'd blow his gun out of his hand and teach him a lesson."

" You mean to say that was a deliberate shot ? "

" Of course. I couldn't miss at that range."

" Holy Cow ! Your shootin's gettin' better than ever," the old man chuckled. " I guess you're a match for anyone in the West by now. You'd better watch out, son. There'll be a few o' the top notchers fair itchin' to take you on if you do any more fancy tricks like that."

Wyatt smiled, but he knew that Cherokee was right. He would have given anything not to have fired on the boy at all. His record of maintaining the Law without gunplay was broken, and his skill was apparent to all. Every man who saw him beat a drawn gun would recount the story with all manner of exaggerations and soon some frontier gunman would get it into his head that he ought to take a crack at Marshal Earp of Witchita. There was no doubt about it—gunplay always bred gunplay, and the less a marshal used his guns the better for all concerned.

Sure enough, the new cattle season hadn't been under way more than a few weeks when a stranger rode into Witchita.

" I hear you've got a marshal who kids himself he's pretty fast with a gun," he told the customers who thronged the bar of the Texan House off Douglas Avenue.

" We sure have, stranger," a townsman answered. " It don't pay to take chances with Wyatt Earp, that's certain."

The stranger snorted with derision. " You ain't seen gunplay yet, my friend," he sneered. " I'm goin' to show that marshal o' yours a thing or two, just as soon as I set eyes on him."

The men in the saloon grinned to each other at the boast, but they were careful not to let the stranger see their smiles—the boaster had a mean look, and a glance at the Navy Colts in his well-worn holsters was enough to tell them he was no man to be trifled with.

" Where are you from ? " the bartender asked, trying his best to break the silence that had fallen on the saloon.

" What's it to you ? "

" I was only asking, stranger, I didn't mean any offence," the bartender protested hurriedly as the gunman glared aggressively across at him.

" Then just stay that way, son," came the reply. " Sergeant King of the Cavalry doesn't like men who asks too many questions."

" Sergeant King ! "

A gasp broke from the saloon's customers as they heard the name. They edged away from the stranger with fear written on their faces. This was no place to be when Sergeant King was in town, for this hard-faced wiry cavalry man was known throughout the West as a ruthless killer—a man who picked quarrels with anyone at the slightest excuse, and settled the argument with the guns he handled so expertly. It was common knowledge that the notorious sergeant liked nothing better than to spend his leaves out of uniform, dressed as a cowboy, for the sole purpose of seeking trouble.

As the townsmen made themselves scarce

Sergeant King took another drink, threw a dollar on to the bar, and walked to the door.

" I'm gunnin' for that marshal right now," he announced as he brushed the bat-wing doors aside and stepped out on to the sidewalk.

Wyatt Earp had been feeling restless all day.

" This town's getting too quiet," he complained to Cherokee as he idled over a steaming mug of coffee in the jailhouse before making his midday rounds of the main streets of Witchita.

Cherokee Watson raised an eyebrow. " You've only got yourself to blame for that, my friend," he remarked wisely. " If you hadn't cleaned up this town so all-fired fast we'd still have plenty o' work on our hands, instead of sittin' here with an empty jail an' nothin' to do."

Wyatt Earp sighed. " Maybe you're right, Cherokee, but that's the only way to handle a marshal's job—hit hard and try to strike first. My old father told me that when I was knee high to a gopher, and it's plain sense. All the same, I don't fancy spending another year in Witchita while there's work to be done all over the West."

Cherokee nodded. " I know what you mean, Wyatt," he agreed. " All this talk of gold being found up in the Nations, and copper in the hills, is enough to unsettle anyone. There was a prospector in town last week told me they're diggin'

solid silver ore out by the ton around Tombstone an' gold at Deadwood. If I was fit I'd
saddle up my old hoss an' have a crack at a spot
o' minin' myself."

" Where's Tombstone ? " Wyatt asked with
interest. " Can't recollect hearing that name
before."

" Over the border in Arizona," Cherokee
informed him. " Seems this town sorta grew
overnight, like a mushroom, after Ed. Schieffelin
struck it rich. He'd been prospectin' for years
up in the barren lands where the only thing that
grows is cactus an' mesquite. He had a hunch
it was silver ore country, but they said he was
crazy. " The only thing you'll find up there will
be your tombstone," they told him. So when he
did strike it rich he called the place Tombstone.
It's just about the wealthiest territory here-
abouts by all accounts. The boys can't dig the
stuff out fast enough to suit the bankers."

It was Wyatt's turn to cock an inquiring look
at Cherokee this time. " How come you know
so much about Tombstone ? " he asked. " You've
been keeping this mighty quiet."

Cherokee had the grace to blush. " Well, it's
like this, Wyatt," he blustered. " I'm gettin'
kinda restless too, an' when a Wells Fargo agent
came in for a chat the other day I asked him
what the chances were o' gettin' a job with his
stage outfit. He offered me a job right then an'

there—up in Tombstone—so I made it my business to ask a few questions."

" Are you going to take the job ? "

Cherokee hesitated. " That depends," he answered slowly.

" On what ? "

" On what you aim to do about bein' the new marshal o' Dodge City," the old man answered with a grin.

For a moment Wyatt was at a loss for words. He thought that no one but the Mayor of Dodge and himself knew anything of the offer he had received that morning by telegraph. Addressed simply to W. Earp, Witchita, the message had reached him within half an hour of being sent. When he opened the paper the wording was plain and to the point :

WE NEED YOU IN DODGE.   TOWN OUT OF CONTROL.   DOUBLE SALARY AND BONUS IF YOU WILL HELP US.   COME AT ONCE.

Wyatt knew that he had shown the paper to no one, in any case he had been too busy thinking over all that the offer implied to waste time discussing it with anyone—least of all an old windbag like Cherokee who liked to know everything about everyone and was the biggest gossip in the territory.

" What d'you know about Dodge ? " he asked

with a touch of anger. "Have you been spyin' on me?"

"Aw shucks, Wyatt. What a thing to say," the old man reproved him. "It just happens that the telegraph clerk is a friend o' mine. He thought I ought to know so that I could advise you against it."

"Why?"

"Because Dodge is so tough it'd need a whole troop o' cavalry to keep order. They pay marshals two hundred dollars a month—but they die so fast there hasn't been a single one who drew more'n fifty dollars from the Mayor."

A slow grin spread over Wyatt Earp's face as he listened to Cherokee's warning.

"What are you grinnin' about?" the old man asked irritably.

"I was just thinkin' I could do with fifty dollars right now," Wyatt told him.

"But you're crazy!" Cherokee blazed. "Man, you won't last a week in Dodge."

"I accepted this morning," Wyatt informed him. "That's something your friend at the telegraph depot *didn't* tell you."

"Then I wash my hands of you!" Cherokee roared. "You haven't got the sense you were born with. No man can clean up Dodge without the Army behind him."

But Wyatt Earp was deadly serious. "I'm sorry, Cherokee," he told his old buffalo-hunting partner. " My mind's made up. I don't want to part bad friends—but I'm going to Dodge within the week. What will you be doing ? "

" Getting away from you and all this fool law officer business ! " Cherokee stormed. " I've had enough o' worryin' my head over you. I'm takin' the Wells Fargo job up at Tombstone." And without another word he stormed out of the empty jail, slamming the door behind him.

Wyatt Earp sat looking sadly at the closed door of the jail for a long while, with sadness in his eyes. Cherokee's outburst had hurt the marshal more than he liked to admit. He was very fond of his old partner ; they had been through many hardships together in the last few years, had faced a score of dangerous situations, and had shared many a joke when things looked black. But now it seemed that their friendship was at an end. Cherokee was as pig-headed as Wyatt himself once his mind was made up, and Wyatt knew in his bones that the old man would take the Wells Fargo job as soon as he left for Dodge—if not sooner.

" Well, I guess that's life," he reflected aloud as he drained his coffee cup and rose to his feet. " No doubt we'll run into one another one of these days—somewhere."

But as Wyatt began his noon patrol through the streets of Witchita the sadness at the loss of an old companion began to give way to other feelings in his mind. He felt a thrill of expectation coursing through his veins as he thought of the task that faced him in Dodge City. Cherokee was certainly right; it would be a full-sized man's job, and one that couldn't be taken on without a lot of thought and courage. The news that filtered up to Witchita from Dodge was bad, very bad. By all accounts the whole township was in uproar, its marshal had headed East on the first available freight train, while his remaining deputies cowered in their homes without daring to walk the streets.

But Wyatt felt more than excitement in the challenge that Dodge City presented to him. He felt a mounting annoyance with Cherokee for his lack of faith in his capabilities. After all it had been Cherokee who persuaded him to take up law enforcement as a career, and now here was the old sinner doing his best to put him off tackling the Dodge job. The more he thought of Cherokee's scathing remarks the more annoyed he felt.

" No man can clean up Dodge without the help of the Army ! " Wyatt repeated to himself. " Nonsense ! If they give me a free hand to pick my own deputies I'll have the trouble makers hogtied within a week. The Army indeed ! Any Mayor who's fool enough to call in the Army to keep the peace would have more trouble on his hands than he ever bargained for. There'd be civil war again in Dodge." He snorted disgustedly at the thought. "The Army indeed! Why they're worse than the Texans with their fancy uniforms, and their swaggering and bugle blowing. I wouldn't give two cents for a whole company of Cavalry—let alone a troop."

It was in this frame of mind that Wyatt Earp arrived at the intersection of Third and Main Streets—just as the glowering Sergeant King of the Cavalry called his name.

"Wyatt Earp!" the Sergeant yelled to the open street. "I'm lookin' for you. Come out and let's see how fast you are!"

Wyatt Earp scarcely paused in his stride as he changed direction and headed for the unseen challenger. He rounded the corner and came face to face with the levelled muzzles of twin forty-fives held in the hands of a tall man in gaudy cowboy clothes.

"I'm Wyatt Earp," he announced in a loud clear voice that rang out across the ten yards of deserted street, as he made a bee line for the man.

The shock of his sudden appearance caught the gunman off guard for an all important moment. Before he could collect his senses the marshal was on him. With a swinging blow he knocked the right hand six-gun flying into the dust, even as his other hand snatched the second forty-five from the sergeant's left hand. Then he brought his right up in a vicious open-palmed slap that knocked the man clean off his feet and threw him to the boards of the raised sidewalk.

Shaking his ringing head the sergeant staggered to his feet with an expression of blank amazement on his face—to find himself staring into the barrel of Wyatt's Peacemaker.

" I'm arresting you for carrying guns within the town's limits, my friend," the marshal informed him with easy nonchalance. " Get moving. The jail's up the block a way."

By now the street had filled with excited onlookers, forsaking the cover of doors and window shutters now that the danger of flying lead was passed.

" Who is he ? " Wyatt called to the nearest man.

It was the bartender from the saloon who answered. " Sergeant King of the Cavalry ! " he whispered in awe-struck tones as he stared at the stern-eyed marshal, and to his surprise he saw a grin crease the corners of Wyatt Earp's mouth.

" The Cavalry ! " he chuckled. " I might have known that useless boaster was an Army man ! "

CHAPTER THIRTEEN

THE DEPUTIES

SERGEANT KING was the last man arrested by Wyatt Earp in Witchita, and yet another trouble-maker who learned the hard way that the tall young marshal had no fear in his make up. To the end of his days he could never explain just what had stopped him from firing as the marshal strode towards him.

" I guess it was the look in his eyes," he was heard to say, and Ben Thompson, Mannen Clements and many others who had stood up to Wyatt Earp with guns in their hands simply nodded their agreement. They knew exactly what the sergeant meant, for they too had met the steely glint in those deep-set eyes. Under the spell of that unblinking stare they had felt like jack rabbits facing a stoat—mesmerised with fear, and utterly powerless to resist. Chero-kee Watson was right; men looked into Wyatt Earp's eyes and knew they were beaten before they started.

But the rioting pleasure-seekers of Dodge City had yet to learn what these men already knew. To them Wyatt Earp was just another marshal, called in to try and curb their twisted ideas of fun. They had heard all about his taming of Thompson, Clements, Peshaur, and King, and had jeered at the Texans who now gave Witchita a wide berth.

"There ain't a marshal born who'll stand up to us," they boasted. "Why, we've run better men than him outa town in two hours. Even Wild Bill Hickok backed down an' left Dodge in a hurry when he was wearin' a badge, an' Mister Wyatt Earp will go the same way if he interferes with us."

But Wyatt Earp bided his time. He slipped into Dodge unheralded, and unrecognised, and reported to the Mayor in private.

"Don't let anyone know I've arrived," he insisted. "I'm not making a move until I'm good and ready. It may be in a few hours, it may not be for a week—but when I think the time's right I'll make these braggarts eat their words."

Mayor Hoover regarded him thoughtfully for a long while.

"What have you got in mind?" he asked at length.

"I want three things," Wyatt told him.

"Name them and if it's humanly possible you shall have them," the Mayor answered promptly.

"Three deputies of my own choosing; a

deadline fixed across town to keep all cattlemen south of the railroad and townsfolk to the north ; and a bonus for every man thrown into jail."

The Mayor frowned, and regarded Wyatt from beneath lowered brows. " I agree to the first two requests—but I'm not too happy about the third. What's the idea, Wyatt ? "

" Just this. I only want that bonus paid on *live* men who've been tamed by me or my deputies. I don't want a bonus on dead men. That way it'll be an incentive to us to arrest rather than kill."

" Tell me more," the Mayor ordered with a twinkle of understanding awakening in his eyes.

" It's like this," Wyatt Earp continued seriously. " You've tried to run Dodge with guns, and it hasn't worked. Your marshals have even shot on sight—just because a man was carrying a gun. That is nothing more nor less than legalised murder, and all it does is breed revenge and more killings. I aim to hurl every man in jail for the smallest offence. I want to *humiliate* these Texans. I want them to know that we can tame them without using our guns. I don't like killing, and I don't want any of my deputies to kill unless it is absolutely essential for their own survival."

The Mayor smiled. " It's a good scheme,

Wyatt," he congratulated his new marshal. " I only hope it works. What amount do you want for the bonus ? "

Wyatt grinned happily. " What do the Texans pay for breaking and taming a wild mustang ? " he asked.

" Two dollars fifty."

" Then I guess you'd better pay the same for taming a Texan," the young peace officer chuckled.

The Mayor roared with laughter at the thought. " That's the best thing I've heard in years," he chortled. " Just wait until those Texans hear about it ! "

But Wyatt Earp had more details to discuss and he cut short the Mayor's laughter. " About these deputies," he said.

" What about them ? Have you any idea who you want ? "

" Yes, I hear Bat Masterson's in town. I want him."

" But he's only twenty-one ! " the Mayor protested.

" I want him," Wyatt answered firmly. " He's the best man with a gun that I know, and he's straight and fair. The second deputy is Billy Tilghman, and the third is Neil Brown."

" Who else do you want ? "

" No one," Wyatt answered promptly. " Three are plenty for the moment."

"What! Man alive, Wyatt, you don't know what you're saying. I've got authority from the City Council to appoint up to twelve deputies as well as a chief deputy. You can't do any good with three men!"

"Three *exceptional* men," Wyatt reminded him with a grin.

Mayor Hoover shrugged his shoulders.

"They'll need to be," he grunted. But Wyatt was insistent that it was quality and not quantity that was needed in his choice of deputies, and after some fruitless argument the Mayor agreed.

Wyatt ran Bat Masterson to earth without much trouble, for wherever that young man chose to stay there was sure to be the noise of ready laughter. Still sticking to his resolve not to be seen in Dodge until he was ready to make his first move, Wyatt sent in word to the gambling hall where Bat was trying his luck with a hand of poker, and soon the two old friends were greeting each other warmly in the comparative secrecy of the livery stables at the rear.

"Wyatt!" the youngster exclaimed as he made out the familiar features of his Kansas City companion in the gloom of the shuttered building. "I've been hearing tales of you and that gun hand o' yours from one end o' the Arkansas to the other. What brings you to Dodge?"

"Trouble," Wyatt told him briefly, yet with a

cheerful smile. " The Mayor asked me to try my hand at running this town the way it should be run. I want you for a deputy. Are you willing ? "

Bat Masterson chuckled. " Now that's a very funny thing, Wyatt," he stated with mock seriousness. " I had a hunch things would start to move pretty soon, and when I heard Wyatt Earp had been sent for I began to behave myself. Now it seems I've been such a good boy these last few weeks I'm going to be rewarded with a job that no one else would take for a fortune. It just doesn't pay to be well-behaved, does it ? "

" You talk too much," Wyatt told him with affection. " How's that trigger finger of yours ? "

" Never been better," Bat confided happily. " I'll take you on any time you like, and give you three seconds start."

Wyatt Earp grinned at the challenge, but he didn't bother to take Bat up on it. Whoever drew against the young adventurer would have to be among the fastest men alive, and although Wyatt knew he was fast himself he was equally sure that he would need a good deal of luck to beat Bat Masterson to the draw.

" I'll take your word for it, Bat," he smiled. " What do you say ? Will you join me ? We pay well, and you get a gold watch after twenty-five years' service ! "

Bat Masterson chuckled. " That settles it," he confirmed. " I had my doubts before, but the gold watch makes all the difference. When do we start ? "

" Just as soon as I've got hold of Billy Tilgh-man and Neil Brown."

" Good. I happen to know where they are. Come along with me and we'll roust out those idle varmints. They'll still be asleep if I know them."

But far from being asleep both Neil Brown and Billy Tilghman were engaged in highly serious business when they found them. Standing before a full-length mirror in their hotel, the two men were going through their daily gun practice—with empty guns. Taking it in turns to rap out the word of command, they went for their Colts with the speed of greased lightning, stopping only to readjust their belts and holsters, before repeating the practice the umpteenth time.

" Having fun, boys ? " Wyatt Earp asked quietly from the doorway, and in a flash both men had twisted round with six-guns levelled at his stomach.

" Wyatt ! " they both cried, almost dropping their guns in their pleasure at the sight of the tall Illinoian.

" What kept you ? " Neil Brown asked as he slipped his Colt back into its holster and took

Wyatt's outstretched hand. His voice had the lilting cadence of an Indian, and the darkness of his features and hair confirmed the fact that Indian blood flowed in his veins.

"Were you expecting me?" Wyatt asked with a grin.

"Of course," Billy Tilghman laughed. "What d'you think we were going to all this trouble for? We've been practising every day since we heard you were coming to Dodge. Where are our badges? We want to start work right away."

"Well, would you believe it!" Wyatt exclaimed in bewilderment. "You must've read my mind before I knew what was in it myself."

"We didn't," came the voice of Bat Masterson from right behind him.

Wyatt Earp turned slowly, a vague glimmering of the truth beginning to seep into his brain. "What do you mean, Bat?" he asked.

"*We* didn't read your mind for you, Wyatt," Bat repeated. "But Cherokee Watson did. He sent word to us that we would be needed, and threatened to come for us with a shotgun if we didn't back your play as Marshal of Dodge. We're here to see you don't get into something you can't get out of. We promised Cherokee, so there's no argument. Speakin' for myself, I'd rather face a grizzly than go against that old buffalo skinner of yours."

" Me, too," echoed Neil Brown and Billy Tilghman with one voice.

If Cherokee Watson could have seen the expression of pleasure and amazement on Wyatt Earp's face when his new deputies told him what the old hunter had done, he would have been more than happy. But next morning, soon after dawn, he would have been happier still, and more than a little proud, to see Wyatt's first day as enforcer of law and order in Dodge City.

The railroad split Dodge in two. South of the tracks lay the cattle camps, the loading yards and corrals, and the rowdier hotels and saloons. North of the tracks lay Front Street—a wide treeless plaza with stores and business premises of all kinds rubbing shoulders with more saloons and gambling houses on the north side, and a bare stretch of hard-packed mud, empty of all buildings, adjoining the tracks. To the east of the Front Street plaza stood the freighting office, locomotive water tanks, and depot building, and to the west more stores and houses of the permanent townsfolk.

Here Wyatt assembled his three deputies and gave his orders.

" I'm setting up a Deadline, boys," he told them. " We can't clean up the whole town, north and south of the tracks, all at once—it's not humanly possible. Besides, the Texans, the

teamsters and the buffalo hunters are entitled
to have their fun in any way they like among
themselves. All we're concerned with is putting
an end to shooting, killing and rioting among
the business houses, and the homes of the
decent townsfolk. We'll fix the Deadline as
being marked by the tracks themselves. North
of that—here in the Front Street Plaza, or anywhere in the main part of town it will be a crime
calling for immediate arrest if any man wears a
gun or disturbs the peace in any way that is a
danger to other folk."

The three men nodded their agreement.

" Sounds sense to me, Wyatt," Billy Tilghman
acknowledged.

" Right. The next thing is shooting. I don't
want a shot fired unless it is absolutely essential.
Don't give a man a chance to go for his gun.
Don't even let him know you are arresting
him if you can help it."

Bat Masterson looked puzzled. " How in
blazes can we do that, Wyatt ? " he queried.

" Easy. Walk past any man you see with a
gunbelt on, and when you're behind him just
tap him on the head with the barrel of your six-
gun," the marshal answered with a grin. " This is
no time to be particular. We're out to enforce the
law and prevent gunplay, and I don't much care
how we do it at first. That's the idea of the
bonus."

" That's what I was going to ask about," Neil Brown broke in. " Who gets the bonus, Wyatt ? "

" All of us, but it will be paid to me. Two dollars fifty for every man we arrest with just cause, providing they're alive. If you have to shoot, then try to wing them, don't shoot to kill. At the end of the month, or whenever you like, we'll split the bonus equally among ourselves. Now get to work—and good luck."

As he spoke Wyatt had seen the first of the visitors to Dodge riding up from the cattle yards—a bunch of newly arrived cowboys dressed up fit to kill, and hurrying to sample the pleasures that Dodge City had to offer them.

Bat Masterson ran his eyes over the approaching horsemen, noting the rakish angle at which their stetsons were tilted, the brilliance of their checkered shirts, embroidered waistcoats, and ornate spurs. Each man wore two six-guns in his silver mounted holsters. " Here comes fifty dollars' worth," he announced with a grin as he counted the twenty riders.

" Wait until they dismount—then take them," Wyatt cautioned.

The horsemen slowed to a walk as they approached the steel tracks of the railroad, the horses stepping high to avoid the rails.

" Morning, marshal," one of them called cheekily as he reached the plaza and dismounted.

He handed his reins to one of his companions who led the horse to the nearest hitching rail along with half a dozen more, while the remaining horsemen rode their own mounts across to take their place at the rail.

"You boys aiming to stay in town long?" Wyatt Earp asked casually as he leaned against the wall of the freighting office.

"As long as we feel like it," the first man answered, swaggering forward with his thumbs crooked through his gunbelt. "What's it to you?" Behind him the rest of his party were all dismounted and had begun to walk towards the Deacon House at the corner of Front Street and Railroad Avenue.

"No guns in town," Wyatt answered quietly.

The cowboy put back his head and guffawed with laughter. "D'you hear what the marshal says, boys?" he called. "No guns in Dodge. If that ain't the funniest thing I've heard!" And as though to demonstrate his amusement with the loudest noise possible, he snatched both guns from his waist and emptied them wildly above his head.

Wyatt waited for the last shot to be fired and then he moved quicker than sight. His Peacemaker flew into his right hand and the seven-inch barrel cracked down on the cowboy's head with the speed of a striking rattlesnake. The man dropped like a stone.

Two of his companions grabbed for their guns, but Bat Masterson beat them to it.

"Watch yourselves," he yelled. "Put up your hands or I'll blast you." And at the sight of his twin guns, combined with those of the other two deputies, the whole party obeyed.

So it went on throughout the day, Bat Masterson chortling happily to himself as the score rose and the bonus tally took shape. By nightfall Dodge City calaboose was crammed to the very walls with disgruntled cowboys, complaining bitterly of their lost freedom, and of the bumps and bruises that were aching so badly on their heads.

Only once did Wyatt resort to gunplay, as a grizzled buffalo hunter moved to cut Bat Masterson in half with his Sharpe's rifle. But he only frightened the man by splintering the stock of his rifle with a carefully aimed bullet, before giving him a tap over the head for good measure and sending him to join the queue at the courthouse.

The deputies and the marshal himself took turns in feeding at the Delmonico restaurant, and Wyatt returned from a brief lunch to find that in his absence his team had stepped up the pressure in an attempt to outdo their chief.

"We missed one, I'm afraid," Billy Tilghman apologised. "We weren't sure what you wanted us to do about the ranchers, so we've stuck to the hired hands only."

Wyatt Earp turned stern eyes on his deputy.
" What do you mean ? " he demanded.

" We saw Bob Rachal carryin' a gun," Tilghman explained hurriedly. " He's a mighty
powerful man, and his trade's worth a mint o'
money to the storekeepers of Dodge. There'll be
trouble if we try and arrest him."

Wyatt Earp didn't smile, a touch of anger
smouldered deep behind his eyes. " You should
have called me, Bill," he reproved the deputy.
" I'll not be a party to any favouritism. All men
must be treated alike, according to the Law.
Where is Rachal now ? "

" Over in a saloon on Second Avenue, and
getting nastier all the time," Neil Brown answered. " He's aimin' to make you pay for the
way you're treating his hands."

" Then I'd better go and tell Mister Rachal
where he gets off," said the Marshal of Dodge
grimly.

CHAPTER FOURTEEN

AMBUSH !

BOB RACHAL woke up next morning with a bump the size of an egg on his head. To his horror he found that he was lying on the floor of Dodge City's jail, surrounded by a collection of unwashed, battered cowboys of all shapes and sizes.

"What happened?" he asked shakily as he looked around.

"You walked right into that new marshal with a gun in your hand," one of his own men informed him. "He's just about the fastest thing on two legs I've ever seen in my life."

Rachal staggered to his feet. "What new marshal?" he asked. "I don't remember anything about it. All I know is that I walked out of the Deacon House, lookin' for a little fun—and I woke up here, in jail. Who is this marshal?"

"Wyatt Earp of Witchita," his hired hand told him.

"Then I'll make it my business to have him fired and run out of Dodge!" the rancher bellowed. "He can't do this to me. My trade

and the money I spend in Dodge are worth more
to this town than any ten outfits you like to
name. You wait 'til I see Mayor Hoover. I'll
make this Wyatt Earp feller wish he'd never
been born."

But Bob Rachal had another shock in store
for him, for when he was hauled unceremoni-
ously before the judge an hour later he was
treated just like any other cowboy. His protests
were silenced by the threat of a further spell
in jail for contempt of court, and he was fined
two hundred dollars for carrying a gun in a
manner contrary to the city ordinances.

When he stormed angrily into Mayor Hoover's
office later he found himself face to face with
the very man who had thrown him into jail.

" I guess you didn't know who I was, young
feller," he roared at the marshal. " You can't
go around arresting men of my importance
like that. Any more nonsense from you and I'll
demand your instant dismissal."

Wyatt Earp eyed him coldly, not even bothering to rise from the edge of the Mayor's desk,
where he had draped his lanky body, with one
leg swinging idly and the other propped against
a chair.

" Is that so ? " he drawled. " As far as I'm
concerned, my friend, you can demand anything
you like. Whether you get it or not is a very
different matter. But all the time I wear a badge

in this town I'll make it my business to slam you into jail for any offence against the peace of this town—whether you're a two-bit cowhand or the President of the United States."

Bob Rachal turned purple in the face with anger. "Mayor Hoover!" he roared when he found his voice. "If this man is still on your pay-roll at this time to-morrow I'll break your town wide open!"

But Mayor Hoover had given Wyatt Earp his personal backing, and he was no man to go against his own word. "I'm sorry, Bob," he answered quietly. "We're going to bring order to this town for the first time in its history. If you don't like it—well—that's too bad. Wyatt Earp has my full support, and I advise you to go back to camp and think it over. Men like you should be an example to your hired hands."

For a moment the rancher stood glowering at the mayor as though he couldn't believe his ears. Then he turned abruptly on his heel and made for the door.

"You'll regret this!" he snarled over his shoulder as he slammed the door behind him.

But threats had no effect on Wyatt's methods of enforcing the law. He proceeded calmly about his duties, always on the alert for trouble, and yet scrupulously fair in all his dealings. Tobe Driskol and other Texas ranchers of similar importance to Bob Rachal suffered the same fate. It made no difference to Wyatt or his deputies who the offender was—they struck fast and hard, buffaloing the culprits across the head with their three-pound Colts, or shooting to wound at the first sign of gunplay. In one short month three hundred men passed through the city jail and Bat Masterson's eyes lit up at the size of the bonus paid out as his share.

" Man ! " he cried when Wyatt handed him the bulging bag of coins. " This beats workin' for a livin' ! "

But it was, in fact, the most gruelling work that Bat or any of his companions had ever encountered. They had to be ready to turn out at a moment's notice at any time of the day or night, whether they were officially on duty or not. They faced deliberate ambushes in the dark alleys of Dodge, and were shot at from cover if they grew careless in standing at a lighted window after dark.

Talk of revenge against the law officers was rife throughout the cattle camps, but few men could be found to match themselves openly against the marshal and his deputies. Those who tried were lucky to escape with their lives, whether they fought the marshals with guns or with bare fists. After two men had been thrashed in one night by Wyatt Earp's iron-hard knuckles the cowboys realised that they were no match for the young Illinoian at any form of fighting, and reluctantly they looked farther afield for some champion to bring to Dodge to lick Wyatt Earp for them.

" I'll willingly pay a thousand dollars to the man who can run this Earp feller out of Dodge," Bob Rachal cried in exasperation one night as he witnessed the return of his foreman, badly mauled and put out of action for many weeks by the marshal's flying fists.

Tempted by this enormous reward several men made attempts on Wyatt's life, choosing their time with care to allow a speedy escape after the killing. They fired from the saddle of a racing horse, or from the darkness of an empty building—but whatever their method of attack they found Wyatt Earp ready, his guns spitting their contempt at the cowardly assassins.

News of the failure of all attempts to rid Dodge City of its incorruptible marshal drifted out to the neighbouring towns and far across the State borders to Arizona, Colorado and deep into the heart of Texas. Soon Wyatt's fame was spreading to the great cities of the East—to New York and Washington, and right along the Atlantic seaboard. The newspapers sent reporters to the lonely cattle town of Dodge to find out for themselves how much truth there was in the rumours of an invincible marshal who had cleaned up Ellsworth and Witchita, and was now three parts of the way to taming Dodge City. They followed the marshal and his deputies about their duties, their pencils busily noting every thing they saw and heard, and soon Wyatt's name was regarded with awe by several million men and women who had never so much as seen a six-gun, and who scarcely knew one end of a horse from another.

Pleased with the way the Dodge City law officers co-operated in providing colour for his reports, one man named Buntline ordered Samuel Colt's factory to make a new six-gun—bigger and better than any other that had so far been designed.

" Here they are," Ned Buntline told the marshal and his deputies as he unpacked the case and drew out the first of the guns. " We'll call them the Buntline Specials. There's one for each of you, and I wish you luck with them."

Wyatt took the revolver in his long-fingered right hand, automatically testing the balance, assessing the weight, and spinning the cylinder with the touch of the expert that he was.

" That's certainly some gun," he said at length, and Buntline's face broke into a happy smile. Coming from Wyatt Earp of Dodge that was praise and thanks indeed.

But Bat Masterson and Billy Tilghman were not so pleased with theirs.

" Just see the length o' that barrel," Bat

exclaimed scornfully as he looked down at his weapon. " It'll take a month o' Sundays to draw from a holster. Why, it must be all of ten inches long ! "

" A good four inches longer than a standard Peacemaker," Tilghman agreed as he compared the two guns. " It's beautifully made, but I don't think it'll be much good for anything but fancy shooting. As you say, Bat, it'll slow us down on the draw, that's certain."

But Wyatt Earp had fallen in love with his Buntline Special the moment he had felt the carved walnut butt in his hand. Fully eighteen inches in length the forty-five-calibre single-action revolver was a man-size gun for a man-size job. And when he saw the special attachment for screwing a rifle stock to the butt to turn it into a long-range weapon his admiration rose to the heights.

" I'm mighty obliged to you, Mr. Buntline," he smiled. " I'll think of you every time I bend this little pacifier over a Texan's head."

And sure enough, the Buntline Special proved its worth in many an encounter with the lawless faction in and around Dodge City.

Admittedly it took a little getting used to, but a few days' practice confirmed Wyatt's opinion— the Buntline Special was supreme as far as he was concerned. With that gun on his right hip, and his old favourite, a Frontier model Colt

Peacemaker on his left hip, he was more than a match for all comers.

One of the first men to learn that the Buntline Special hadn't slowed down the marshal's draw was the dreaded Clay Allison. Arriving in Dodge at the express wish of the Texan ranchers, this killer lost ro time in challenging the marshal in full daylight outside Wright and Beverley's store on Front Street. Minutes later he was headed back across the tracks, wiser in the knowledge that Wyatt Earp had rammed the twelve-inch barrel of his Buntline Special into his stomach while his own gun was barely half-way out of its holster. Next time he wanted to visit Dodge on business he asked permission of the marshal first!

And yet the Texan cattlemen were still determined that Wyatt Earp should pay for his interference with their liberties and ideas of fun. When it became apparent that single-handed action against the law officer was of little use, they changed their tactics.

Wyatt was busy to the north of Dodge one night when the sound of rapid firing and yelling came to him from south of the tracks. He arrived breathless in Front Street to find a dozen cowboys riding up and down the main street at breakneck speed, firing furiously at every pane of glass and light in sight.

Wyatt kept to the shadows, approaching on

cat-feet until he had sized up the situation, and identified the ringleaders. And all the time he looked for an indication that one or more of his deputies was available to back him.

As he crept nearer he recognised the burly figure of Tobe Driskol and another man named Morrison, whilst some of the other riders were vaguely familiar to him as members of the Rachal and Driskol outfits.

A movement from the Long Branch saloon caught Wyatt's eye.

" I guess that's Bat and the boys waiting their chance," he smiled to himself—but for once the marshal was wrong. Unknown to him his deputies had been drawn off to the other side of town by a feint attack, leaving the marshal of Dodge to handle this incident alone.

Convinced that he had the backing of his fellow marshals Wyatt threw all caution to the winds. In his experience surprise had always been half the battle when dealing with rampaging gunmen, and this looked like an occasion when it would pay him to reveal himself with the greatest degree of surprise he could manage.

Still keeping to the shadows of the buildings he strode along the sidewalk, making for the closed doors of the Long Branch where he knew there was a loaded shotgun within reach of his hand, and where he imagined Bat Masterson or one of the boys would be ready and waiting to help.

Even as he reached the door and was stooping to reach inside for the butt of the shotgun, the worst happened. A flying bullet smashed into a shutter above him, breaking the catch, and sending a stream of vivid golden light directly down upon him.

Temporarily blinded by the glare, Wyatt fumbled awkwardly, and next instant a shout of triumph rose up from the street as he was spotted by Tobe Driskol.

" It's Earp ! By Heaven we've got him ! " the rancher roared, springing on to the sidewalk directly in Wyatt's path, with twin revolvers gleaming in his hands.

A cold chill touched Wyatt's spine. He straightened slowly, his arms raised and his hands carefully held away from the butt of his Buntline Special and the old Peacemaker.

" I've got the drop on you at last, Earp ! " the rancher jeered as he stepped forward surrounded by his men. " You walked right into this one, and now it's my turn to even the score."

" Killing me won't help you, Driskol," Wyatt countered, trying valiantly to make his voice normal and hide the dryness of his mouth. " Bat Masterson will hound you from one end o' the States to the other, and there'll be a hundred men to ride with him. Put up your guns and learn some sense."

As he spoke Wyatt was listening to every sound in the saloon behind him. He heard the quick, muffled tread of booted feet from the other side of the door, but still no deputies made their appearance, nor was there any further sound as the seconds dragged by on leaden feet.

Driskol moved nearer, his face illuminated oddly by the shafts of light that still streamed through the broken shutter.

" Pray, marshal ! " he spat out with relish, the knuckles of his right hand whitening at the fierceness of his grip. " This is when you die—you Northern Yankee ! "

CHAPTER FIFTEEN

DOC. HOLLIDAY INTERVENES

WYATT EARP stood frozen in his tracks, scarcely daring to breathe. Inwardly he cursed himself for being so careless. Time and again he had driven the point home to his deputies that they must always make sure they could manage a situation before they moved into action. And now here was he, out-manœuvred and defenceless, at the mercy of a dozen armed Texans who had scant respect for their own lives—let alone that of a marshal.

He opened his mouth to speak, but the words wouldn't come out, and he knew deep down inside him that nothing he could say would be of the slightest use. Tobe Driskol was about to kill him in cold blood.

" Pray, marshal ! " the rancher repeated, gloating over the words.

And then the miraculous happened. The door of the saloon swung open behind Wyatt's back to reveal a small dark-haired stranger with deep-set eyes that blazed with an intense fire. Two guns were gripped, firm and steady, in his hands—one a nickel-plated Colt, and the other a battered forty-four.

" Drop those guns, you murdering coyote ! "

The little man's voice rose high pitched like a scream, knifing through the sudden silence like the swish of a whiplash. Driskol started as though he had been struck, and his guns clattered to his feet and fell to the boards of the sidewalk.

Wyatt didn't wait to identify his saviour. He darted sideways under the man's very nose and grabbed for the shotgun hidden behind the door. His hand closed on empty air.

" Take this, Wyatt ! " a voice yelled in his ear, and he saw the stock of a heavy scatter-gun held out to him from the darkness of the saloon. Without thinking he snatched it up, slamming both hammers back as he moved and swung to face the Texans at the side of his rescuer.

One of the cowboys at the rear went for his gun, but the nickel-plated Colt spat once in the stranger's hand and the man staggered back with a scream, clutching wildly at his shoulder.

" Another move and I'll mow you down," Wyatt roared, finding his lost voice in a wild surge of relief. " Up with those hands— high and empty ! "

Racing footsteps thudded down the street as the cowboys obeyed, and a voice called urgently from the darkened street, " Wyatt ! Wyatt ! Are you all right ? "

Wyatt Earp recognised Bat Masterson's voice.

" Everything under control, Bat," he yelled gaily in reply. " Fetch a sack for all these guns, and lead the way to the jail."

Bat appeared suddenly in the circle of light, perspiration pouring down his face from his running, and behind him Neil Brown padded to a halt on moccasined feet.

Bat gulped, as much from amazement as from lack of breath. " Holy Cow ! " he gasped. " Looks like you've had quite a party, Wyatt. Why didn't you wait for us ? "

But Wyatt was too busy to bother his head with Bat Masterson's wisecracks. " Grab their guns and throw them all in the calaboose," he ordered. " And take good care of Driskol— I want a few words in private with that rattle-snake. I'll join you later—right now I've got some thanks to get off my chest."

He turned to express his appreciation to the stranger for the prompt action that had un-doubtedly saved his life, but to his surprise the man had disappeared. In his place stood the towering portly figure of Chalk Beeson, owner of the Long Branch.

" Where's he gone ? " Wyatt demanded.

" Back to his poker game I shouldn't wonder," Beeson chuckled. " That hombre's just about the coolest customer I've ever met."

" Who is he ? "

" Doc. Holliday—the gunfighting dentist,"

Chalk Beeson answered with something approaching awe in his voice.

Doc. Holliday was seated at the far end of the saloon when Wyatt Earp pushed his way through the excited crowd that had gathered and entered the Long Branch. Fresh lanterns had been lighted and were hanging from the ceiling hooks, illuminating the shattered windows, cracked mirrors and broken bottles that littered the floor. Wyatt paused by the bar, staring at the little stranger whose name was so familiar.

" So this is the famous Doc. Holliday," he muttered to himself as he studied the stranger's stooped shoulders, and sunken, fever-ridden cheeks. He watched as Doc. Holliday broke the band from a new pack of cards and riffled them through his fingers in a lightning shuffle. And then he caught the Doctor's eye and walked across to him.

" I'm obliged to you, Doctor," he said simply, holding out his hand.

The little man looked down at his cards, ignoring the outstretched palm. " For what ? " he asked gruffly with a pronounced Southern drawl.

Wyatt was taken aback. " For saving my life out there," he replied with a gesture towards the street. " That's the nearest I've ever been to death, and believe me I shan't forget what you did."

Doc. Holliday's eyes forsook the cards, focusing slowly on the marshal's face. For a long time he sat there staring at the man he had saved from the Texans.

" You're a fool ! " he drawled eventually. " Do you think I'd bother my head over a marshal ? Whether you or any other peace officer is killed is of no interest to me."

This was too much for Wyatt Earp. " Then why in blazes did you intervene ? " he demanded angrily.

" Because that no good, yellow-livered, ornery, pie-bald, addle-headed, ignorant bunch of four-flushing, two-bit prairie dogs interrupted my poker game when I was winning ! " the little man spluttered with ill-concealed rage.

Wyatt Earp saw a lot of the gambling dentist in the months that followed. There was something about the little man that fascinated him. He spent hours sitting in the Long Branch saloon while the Doctor demonstrated his skill with cards to all comers, gambling vast amounts on the little pieces of pasteboard, his drooping moustache wilting with dejection as the luck went against him, or bristling fiercely as Lady Fortune aided his efforts. A creature of moods, the Doctor was never the same two days running.

" He's a dying man," Chalk Beeson muttered

to Wyatt as they saw the Doctor doubled up with a paroxysm of coughing on one occasion. "He hardly eats enough to keep a flea alive, and drinks enough for twenty men. I wouldn't give him more than a year or two on this Earth, and when he goes there will be few who mourn for him."

Wyatt frowned. "What's the matter with him, Chalk?" he asked.

"Consumption. He came West for his health, but the way he lives would cripple a healthy man—let alone an invalid. Steer clear of him, Wyatt. He's a madman—a southern gentleman gone wrong. All he lives for is his endless poker playing, strong likker and the chance to show off his marksmanship with that nickel-plated Colt of his."

"Hasn't he got any friends?" the marshal queried.

Chalk Beeson laughed. "Friends?" he repeated scornfully. "There's not a man in the West has any love for Doc. Holliday. His name's poison in every settlement from Arkansas to the Canadian border. He's mean, unpredictable, and a merciless killer when he's roused. No, sir! Doc. Holliday doesn't make friends—only enemies."

"That's not true, Chalk," Wyatt answered quietly. "The Doctor's made one friend for life—Wyatt Earp of Dodge." And with that the marshal turned on his heel and went to join Bat Masterson.

Bat was pacing up and down the sidewalk outside the telegraph office with a paper in his hands, frowning every time he glanced at it.

" What's the trouble ? " Wyatt asked as he approached.

" It's that old buffalo-skinner of yours, Wyatt," the deputy exclaimed.

" Who—Cherokee ? "

Bat nodded. " He's wired from Tombstone to say things are really poppin' up there. Wants me to go and join him."

A slow smile broke over Wyatt's face. " Wants *you* to join him ? " he chuckled.

Bat Masterson looked up with sudden understanding. " So *that's* what the old sinner is after ! " he exclaimed. " He's askin' *me* and meaning *you*. I guess he's too proud to tell you he's in trouble after the argument he had with you. Here, take a look, Wyatt, and tell me what you think."

Wyatt Earp took the telegraph form and scanned it quickly.

BAT MASTERSON DODGE CITY. IF YOU LIKE FIREWORKS COME TO TOMBSTONE. SHERIFF BEHAN HAS TOO MANY FRIENDS.
                                    CHEROKEE WATSON

Wyatt started at the name Behan. "That's the marshal I fell foul of up at George Ulrick's place," he told Bat. "I wonder what Cherokee's getting at? It's not like him to ask for help unless things are really bad. Is he still working for Wells Fargo on the stage line?"

"As far as I know he is," Bat answered. "Last I heard he was riding shotgun on the bullion coaches from the mines. That could be a pretty lively little job if the road agents are up there in force."

Wyatt frowned. "And if this Behan feller is too friendly with them," he added grimly, "I guess the sooner we get up there and find out for ourselves the better."

"Suits me," agreed Bat Masterson without hesitation.

But it was some time before Wyatt could be spared from his duties in Dodge. He had given his word to the new Mayor, Dog Kelly, that he would see out the cattle-shipping season as marshal, and his hands were full with a fresh batch of strangers accompanying the cattle. He was determined to leave Dodge completely tamed, and stuck grimly to his agreement with the Mayor.

"You'd better hit the trail for Tombstone," he told Bat Masterson. "Find out what you can and wire me any news. I'll do my best to clear things up here by the end of the season anyway.

Then I'll be free to join you, or try my luck somewhere else. Dodge hasn't enough excitement to offer me now. Why, take a look at me! I'm wearing city gent's clothes and flat-heeled shoes. If I stay much longer I'll end up behind the counter of a store!"

Bat Masterson laughed. "Come to think of it, Wyatt, you do look like a prosperous storekeeper. Several times I've almost mistaken you for your brother Morgan. You're the split living image of him with that black tail-coat, and the string tie. Wonder what he's doin' these days?"

"Last I heard he was headed West with brother Virgil," Wyatt told him, stroking his flourishing handlebar moustache thoughtfully. "It'd be good to see those boys again, but I guess it'll be years before we meet. They're like me— they've got itchy feet, and just don't seem to be able to stop any one place for long."

But Wyatt was to meet both his brothers much sooner than he expected, for when Bat Masterson's wire came through from Tombstone it stated briefly that Virgil Earp was town marshal of the town, and Morgan Earp was due to join him at any minute. Beyond that the message simply stated that there was work for a Buntline Special!

Wyatt packed his kit at once.

"Seems I'm being asked to join the family

business," he grinned to Mayor Kelly as he took his leave. " With Virgil *and* Morgan up at Tombstone we'll have to call ourselves ' Law-enforcers Incorporated ' I guess ! "

Dog Kelly smiled. " I feel kinda sorry for the trouble-makers in Tombstone," he said dryly. " Go easy with them for a bit, Wyatt, or the shock might be too much for them."

" I'm not a marshal any longer, don't forget," Wyatt Earp answered as he swung up on to the driving seat of the stage and settled himself as comfortably as he could alongside the whisk-ered driver.

" You soon will be," Dog Kelly prophesied. " Good luck—and don't forget, we'll give you your old job back anytime you like. There'll always be a welcome for you in Dodge City."

" Depends whether it's a Kansas welcome, or a Texas welcome," the ex-marshal of Dodge grinned back, as the driver swung his rawhide whip high above this head, and cracked it viciously over the backs of the lead horses of his team.

CHAPTER SIXTEEN

THE TOMBSTONE STAGE

THE Wells Fargo coach made good time across the open prairie lands around Dodge City, but soon the going grew harder and the speed dropped.

Sitting beside the driver Wyatt Earp found himself bounced and jerked about on the hard wooden seat until every bone in his body ached.

" I'd rather ride an unbroken bronc, any day," he complained bitterly to the driver as a sudden lurch threatened to unseat him completely.

But the bewhiskered teamster only grinned. " You ain't seen nothin' yet, Mister," he said cheerfully. " Wait 'til we get up into the brush country. You never know what you're goin' to find next. Last trip we hit a river in flood, two fallen trees across the trail, and broke a wheel on a rock ten miles from the nearest stagin' house. An' we drove into Tombstone dead on time," he added proudly.

Wyatt whistled through his teeth. " You're making me wish I'd travelled inside with the other passengers, instead of perching up here like a bear out on a limb," he groaned. " How far's the first stagin' point ? "

"About twenty-five miles," the driver told him. "We'll be lucky if we make it by sundown, an' the hosses'll be about dead beat by then. One hour's stop to hitch on a fresh team, pick up any more passengers an' freight, an' then we're off again."

"When do we sleep?" the marshal exclaimed.

"You don't, Mister. This is a non-stop trip. "We're carryin' 20,000 dollars in coin for the minin' camps in the boot. That's why Johnny Shotgun is lookin' so all-fired anxious. He's got a regular arsenal laid out beside him in case o' trouble."

Wyatt glanced over his shoulder, and saw for the first time the head and shoulders of the stage guard rising above the rear of the coach and peering at him over the bundles and boxes of baggage and freight that littered the roof.

"Expecting trouble?" Wyatt yelled.

The shotgun rider shrugged his shoulder expressively. "Can't say, marshal," he roared back. "But the road agents are pretty active up in the hills, and you never know when they're goin' to strike. It don't pay to take chances."

Wyatt climbed off the seat, bracing himself carefully against the rocking and lurching of the coach, and crawled over the roof to join the guard.

"Mighty fine collection of guns you've got there," he remarked appreciatively as he dropped down on to the boot and saw the display of fire-arms arranged within easy reach of the guard's hands.

"Not bad," the man admitted. "A sawn-off Wells Fargo shotgun for close-range work—loaded ten buckshot to each barrel; a Winchester repeater for long shots; and a coupla Navy Colts thrown in for good measure. The driver's got a Winchester and a couple six-guns as well tucked away up front. I've known the time when we needed every durned one o' them. One trip we ran from Tombstone to Tucson we blazed off a hundred an' fifty round atween us before the road agents had enough."

"When was that?" Wyatt queried with interest, yelling loudly to make himself heard above the noise of the coach's progress.

"When we took the spring clean up from the mines for bankin'," the other told him. "We had nigh on two hundred thousand dollars' worth o' bullion that trip, an' half the wild boys in the territory were after us. But it was the Blackburn gang we were scared of, they wouldn't leave us alone all the way through the hill country. The U.S. Marshal's posse broke up the gang a week or two later, but they do say some o' the Blackburn riders are workin' in with the Clantons an' McLowerys now. That's who we're on the watch for this trip. They're poison."

The names were new to Wyatt, and he soon lost

interest in the guard's endless tales of ambushes by masked men, and successful battles with bandits of all kinds. All he was interested in was getting to Tombstone as quickly as possible, to meet the two brothers he hadn't seen for years, and to check with Bat Masterson and Cherokee Watson on whatever it was that was causing them concern.

" Know anything about Sheriff Behan ? " he asked the guard suddenly.

" Johnny Behan ? " The man spat expressively into the dust of the trail. " That feller's so two-faced you don't know his back from his front. Every man he arrests manages to break jail over-night, and if he's a member o' the Clanton crowd he's out long afore that ! Don't talk to me about Johnny Behan—he's nothin' but a hired hand of Ike Clanton."

So that was what Cherokee was hinting at ! Wyatt pricked up his ears and pumped the guard for all he was worth. Twenty minutes later— his tiredness and aching bruises forgotten—the ex-marshal of Dodge climbed down from the boot at the first staging stop, with a complete picture of the troubles of Tombstone in his mind. Cutting out all the colourful exaggeration that the guard had added to his story, it was plain that Cherokee had walked right into a hornet's nest.

But Wyatt was not to be allowed to digest his

new-found knowledge in peace for long, for as he stretched his long legs and joined the other passengers, who crowded the doorway of the stage house in search of coffee and food, a familiar figure rounded the corner of the building.

" Doc ! " Wyatt exclaimed in wonder. " What in tarnation are you doing so far from Dodge ? "

Doc. Holliday walked towards him, his grey frock-coat flaring out in the breeze to reveal the black tooled-leather of the gunbelt at his waist. Even as he approached a fit of coughing seized him, and he halted, fighting for breath.

" Heard you were leavin' Dodge, Mister Earp," he gasped as the fit passed. " I didn't fancy that one-horse township without you to keep things nice and peaceful for a little earnest gambling, so I rode to pick up the stage here, and join you in Tombstone. Any objections ? "

The last words were stated more as a challenge than as a question, but Wyatt Earp ignored the little man's aggressive tone.

" I guess card-playing is much the same in any town," he said quietly. " But watch that gun hand of yours in Tombstone, Doctor, my brother Virgil is town marshal, and he's mighty hard on gunfighters. He was fast five years ago, and I reckon he hasn't lost any speed since then."

Doc. Holliday bowed exaggeratedly in mock

courtesy. " I'm obliged to you for the warning, marshal," he acknowledged, as he climbed up to take his seat inside the coach.

It was a trick of the sun, catching the steel of a stirrup iron, that gave them warning of the ambush ahead.

The coach had slowed to a snail's pace as it wound up the incline among the huge red boulders and weeping cottonwoods that fringed the trail. The horses plodded gamely on, throwing their shoulders into the traces and digging their steel-shod hooves deep into the firm ground as they fought to haul the heavy, creaking stagecoach to the brow.

The driver raised his whip to urge the team to a final effort, but the guard's warning cry checked him before he could flick it forward.

" In the trees—to the left ! " The shotgun rider yelled, grabbing for his Winchester as twelve men sprang into view, poised for a second in full view of the trail before careering madly down into the cover of the trees.

Wyatt Earp sat up with a jerk. He had been drowsing on the roof of the coach, his wide black hat covering his face as he tried to snatch a brief respite from the rigours of the journey. His Buntline Special flashed into his right hand, barking twice at the dense stand of timber. A third report sounded behind him as the guard brought his Winchester into action and blazed at the hidden riders.

" Giddup there, you four-legged, long-eared, sons of Satan ! " the driver roared, lashing at the frightened horses as they checked in their stride. The team recovered, neighing its resentment to the heavens, and breasted the ridge just as the riders cleared the trees and made for the final slope.

" Give 'em their heads ! " Wyatt yelled at the driver. " Use your whip and let 'em go. We'll handle this." As he spoke he was reaching for the spare Winchester. He flicked the lever, pumping a shell into the breech, flung the rifle to his shoulder and fired at the leading horsemen.

" Missed ! " he muttered angrily, as the coach swayed and spoilt his aim. He heard the bullet strike a rock between the horses' legs and go whining off into the trees with a jeering ricochet. He flung himself flat, steadying the rifle as best he could against the baggage rail of the coach, and squeezed the trigger again.

This time a yelp of pain came back to him, and he saw with grim satisfaction the first rider fold suddenly in his saddle and let go his horse's rein.

" One up to you ! " chortled the voice of the guard as he groped his way across the roof to join Wyatt. " Now it's my turn."

But the road agents had broken off, swinging

back into the cover of the trees after their warm reception.

" They'll be back," Wyatt grinned. " Then we'll see what sort of hand *you* are with a Winchester."

By now the team of horses was well into the descent, racing forward at breakneck speed as the driver gave them their head. Faster and faster they went, eating up the trail with their flying hooves, the lather forming thick and white on their flanks.

" How are we doin' ? " called the driver urgently. " I can't let these critturs run like this much longer—they'll break a leg or turn us over at the next twist in the trail."

" We're safe for a while," Wyatt called back. " Rein 'em in, but keep goin' as fast as you dare."

The bandits struck again as they reached the levels of the valley bottom and the trail widened out.

They came from both sides, riding low to their horses' necks in Indian fashion, their hats off to lessen the target. Wyatt took careful aim and fired quickly, but the bullet went wide again. He glanced at the Winchester suspiciously— He could have sworn he was right on target. With an expression of disgust he saw the backsight was out of alignment, and the gun was thick with grime and dust.

"Don't you ever clean these things?" he scowled, throwing the gun from him angrily and whipping his Buntline out once again.

The guard didn't answer. He was too busy firing at a horseman who had appeared suddenly on the far side and was far too close for comfort. Wyatt saw the rider straighten in the saddle and level his own gun, ignoring the bullets that were hurled at him. There was a tiny spurt of flame, then another, and the guard jerked backwards, his Winchester falling with a clatter on to the trail.

Wyatt swung his Buntline forward in line with his waist, like a pointing finger, and blasted the horseman from his saddle.

But other riders were closing fast and bullets were beginning to smack into the baggage all around, splintering the wood of packing cases, and driving clear through the softer goods.

Wyatt bent over the guard's body, fumbling for his heart. He could feel no reassuring movement. The man was dead.

"You murdering devils!" he muttered, his eyes glinting coldly as he took aim at the nearest rider.

As he fired a fusilade of shots rapped out from the windows of the coach where the passengers had joined the battle. He glanced down and saw the glowering face of Doc. Holliday appear at one window.

" Give me a hand, marshal ! " the little man cried. " I'm comin' to join you." And without more ado the Doctor climbed out of the window, grasped Wyatt's outstretched hand and hauled himself up on to the roof.

" That's better," the little man exclaimed, seating himself carefully on a bullet-scarred trunk, and brushing his tails out carefully behind him. " Now we're all set for a little target practice."

And right there and then Doc. Holliday proceeded to give an exhibition of shooting that Wyatt Earp had rarely seen equalled. His nickel-plated Colt stuttered its message of death with unerring aim. In as many seconds Wyatt saw two riders topple from their saddles, and a third shot crease the hindquarters of a galloping horse. He found himself motionless, his own gun forgotten as he watched the gunfighting dentist perform.

In minutes the attack was over—the last of the bandits racing out of range, and away into the scrub land to the north.

" I guess I'd better warn Virgil, not you, Doc.," said Wyatt with a grin.

CHAPTER SEVENTEEN

CHEROKEE'S SURPRISE

" WE'RE mighty grateful to you and Doc. Holliday, Wyatt," said the Tombstone Wells Fargo agent as he stacked the pay-roll money into the safe and slammed the door shut thankfully. " This hold-up business is getting worse all the time. What will happen when the next large bullion shipment leaves the mines I don't dare to think."

" I only did what any other man with a gun would have done," Wyatt answered modestly. " It was Doc. Holliday who finished off the battle for us. All I'm sorry about is the loss of a good man back there on the trail. The pay-roll money can go hang as far as I'm concerned."

The agent sighed dejectedly. " I know, that's the third man we've lost this season. Soon we shan't be able to recruit new guards. We pay them well, but things are hotting up all the time, and a good many men have turned down the job already. I don't really blame them either. Riding shotgun on a bullion coach isn't my idea of a long-term career ! "

" What's the Law doing about it ? " Wyatt demanded.

" Precious little. Robbery of a mail coach is a federal matter, and only a United States Marshal can handle it—with the help of a local sheriff. Your brother Virgil is town marshal, and his hands are tied, he can't act without being specially deputised by the federal man, or by Johnny Behan. And I guess you realise there's little love lost between those two. Virgil and Behan are at each other's throats all the time."

" That's no way to clean up the territory ! " Wyatt protested. " I guess I'd better have a word with Virgil and see what *is* going on up here."

The Wells Fargo man held up his arm to detain the ex-marshal of Dodge. " How about working for us ? " he asked.

Wyatt Earp paused in the doorway. " In what capacity ? "

" Anything you like to call yourself. What we need is someone of your reputation to ride on the special bullion runs, to investigate any attacks on the company's property or passengers, and to generally keep an eye on our interests."

" I'll think it over," Wyatt told the agent as he went off in search of his brother.

He found Virgil at the town marshal's office and received a welcome that warmed his heart. For hours the two brothers swapped news of their adventures since the family had come West in '64.

" Seems we're all gathering in Tombstone," Virgil Earp commented as he came to the end of his recital. " I've taken mining rights here and Morgan is arriving from Montana to help. Brother Jim is headed this way too, and now *you* come under your own steam. It must be an omen ! "

Wyatt grinned. " I shouldn't wonder, Virgil. It's been a mighty long time since we were all together, and from what I hear this little township's going to need a few Earps around. I was offered a job with Wells Fargo the minute I arrived—what do you think I should do ? "

" Take it," Virgil advised. " I'll get you sworn in as a deputy sheriff for the county, and you can work both jobs together."

It was only then that Wyatt realised he hadn't located Bat Masterson. There had been no sign of the youngster since he arrived in Tombstone.

" Where's Bat ? " he asked.

Virgil laughed. " He's gone haring off to Deadwood to try his luck at the new gold strike. He'll be back with his tail between his legs soon—only a few lucky ones strike it rich these days."

" I thought you said *you* were mining ? " Wyatt commented dryly.

" Oh, that's different," his brother answered at once. " Tombstone's built right on top of the richest silver deposits ever struck. There's a big hole in the end of the main street where they dug out pure silver, and the mines all around are striking ore assaying fifteen thousand to twenty thousand dollars a ton. You can't go wrong here ! "

" I'll take your word for it," Wyatt smiled. " Me, I'd rather stick to the only trade I know. Just you get me that appointment and I'll be happy. There's not much I haven't learned about handling lawbreakers since I rode into Ellsworth with Cherokee Watson."

" Did someone take my name in vain ? " came a growling voice from the doorway of the office.

Wyatt whirled around, a wide smile breaking over his face.

" Cherokee ! " he cried.

" Wyatt, you young scamp ! I've been lookin' all over for you. Hear you had a spot of bother on the trail in," the old buffalo hunter answered, punching his ex-partner in the chest with obvious affection. " Bat Masterson said you would hit the trail for Tombstone afore long. It's good to see your ugly face again."

" It's good to see you too, Cherokee. I've missed you—I nearly got myself shot up in Dodge a while back without you to look after me."

" Serves you right," Cherokee grunted. " But

I guess you've jumped outa the frying pan into the fire. Have you told him what goes on up here in Tombstone, Virgil ? "

Virgil Earp shook his head. " Not yet, Cherokee. We've had so much to talk about I haven't got round to it yet."

" Then I'd best tell him straight away," the old hunter said firmly, " else he'll never know anything important."

Cherokee Watson's outline of events in Tombstone and the surrounding territory didn't make good hearing. Much of it Wyatt had already learned, but he listened attentively, turning once or twice to Virgil for confirmation of the more highly coloured facts, but never breaking the old man's flow of words.

" It's like this, Wyatt," Cherokee began. " Tombstone's like a water hole in a blazin' desert. There's more money to the square inch in this stinkin' hole than all the rest of Arizona put together. So what happens ? Every two-bit gambler, gunman, an' murderin' coyote for miles around crowds in to feed on the pickin's. There's precious little law, an' no order."

" On top o' that," the old man went on, warming to his theme, " there's the biggest crowd o' rustlers, outlaws, stage robbers, an' general ne'er-do-wells in Creation spread out all around us—the Clanton-McLowery gang. Why, man, I've been shot at every time I've ridden a bullion coach outa Tombstone! *And nothing's being done about it !*"

Cherokee paused for breath and for his words to sink in.

" Virgil's tried to clean up the town itself," he went on after a pause. " But every time he arrests a man he has to turn him over to Sheriff Behan for trial. Then all that happens is that the jail gets broken open, an' the prisoner runs off to join the Clantons."

" What, *every* time ? " Wyatt exclaimed.

" Yes," Virgil admitted. " There've been a hundred and three arrests since I've been here, and a hundred and three escapes! It sounds crazy, but it's true. Every move I make is blocked by that conniving Sheriff. If I go to arrest a man outside the town limits, he stops me and tells me I haven't any authority—the county offences come under him. If I try to spur him into doing something about the stage hold-ups, he just laughs, and tells me it's a federal offence and the United States Marshal must handle it."

" Who's the federal marshal," Wyatt broke in.

" There's no one assigned to Pima County or Cochise County," Virgil answered ruefully. " There's a senior marshal appointed by the Governor of the State of Arizona, and he's a good man, but of course he's got his hands full and we don't see him from one month to the next. By the time he can organise a posse the outlaws are across the border into Mexico. It's as simple as that."

A chuckle from Cherokee brought both men's eyes round in surprise.

" What are you laughing about, Cherokee ? " Wyatt Earp asked with sudden suspicion.

" Nothin' much," Cherokee gurgled. " Except that Virgil's got it all wrong. There *is* a new deputy United States Marshal for this Territory."

" That's a new one on me," Virgil exclaimed, eyeing the old man oddly. " Who is he ? "

" Wyatt Earp," the old hunter said abruptly. " I fixed it up on the last trip to Tucson. All he's got to do is sign on, take the oath and the job's his ! "

" Well I'll be hanged ! " Wyatt laughed. " I never know what you're going to be up to next ! "

Wyatt Earp's appointment as deputy United States Marshal was confirmed within days, the federal authorities nearly falling over themselves in their hurry to swear in the famous Marshal of Dodge City before he changed his mind.

" There's only one thing that's bothering me," Wyatt commented as he accepted the badge of his new office.

" What's that ? "

" Just what are my duties ? What crimes am I responsible for ? "

" Any crime that interferes with the carriage of Government Mail; and offences involving desperadoes, rustlers or horse thieves who cross the State border," he was told. " You have the power to deputise men to assist you, singly or as a posse, and you may be called upon to assist the County Sheriff, or the Town Marshal should they need you."

" Can I take another job as well ? " Wyatt asked.

" That depends on what job it is. You must be available for federal services as and when needed, but the rest of the time you are free to do what you like. What job have you in mind ? "

" Wells Fargo want me to act for them in connection with stage robberies," the new marshal replied. " Do you agree to that ? "

" Couldn't be better, marshal. In that position you can keep a close watch on the Mails—Wells Fargo have the contract for carrying them, and the fact that you are looking after their interests as well is an added advantage."

" Good, then I'll get straight to work," Wyatt answered.

It was a long ride back from Tucson to Tombstone. The trail passed through waterless desert country in which the only vegetation was the isolated clumps of giant cactus, standing higher than horse and rider combined. Like enormous human hands sprouting abruptly from the sand and alkali dust, the cacti fingered upwards to the blazing sun, as silent markers of the trail.

Wyatt felt the heat beating down upon him with a burning intensity. The perspiration dried on his forehead as soon as it appeared, and the endless dust billowed up in the motionless air, filling his nostrils, and working its way clear through his clothes.

" What a country ! " he repeated for the twentieth time as he halted his weary horse and gazed anxiously about for sign of water.

Far ahead where the first slopes of the foothills descended to the desert, he spotted a small stand of mesquite thorn, and beyond it another— larger.

" If that's not a sign of water you can call me a no-good Texan," he muttered to himself, urging his horse forward, and soon he was gratefully bathing his face in spring water that bubbled up from beneath a grotesquely shaped boulder. He cupped his hand to take a mouthful of water, but stopped with surprise. He had only just noticed that his horse had barely touched its lips to the water, before moving off to nibble at the scant grass that carpeted the banks of the spring.

That was odd. Wyatt looked about him, and

realised with something of a shock that the trees shading the place were not as big as one would expect so close to water ; the grass was a dirty brownish colour ; and the soil itself looked dull and lifeless. He took a little water in his hand and smelt it.

" Smells all right to me," he murmured, but when he gingerly dipped the tip of his tongue into his cupped hand, he drew back with a grimace of disgust.

" Salt ! " he complained bitterly, spitting out the thick, brackish liquid. " I ought've known better ; this is alkali country." He rose sadly to his feet, retrieved the reins of his horse and climbed back into the saddle with weary resignation. " You've got more sense than me, hoss," he smiled to the lathered animal. " I guess there's nothing for it but to make tracks for Tombstone, and forget our thirst 'til we get there."

But Wyatt's drink was to be delayed even longer than he thought, for when at last he came out on the ridge of the Dragoon Mountains, high above Tombstone, he saw at once that all was not well in the Township. Scattered puffs of gunsmoke rose up all along the main street, and the distant crackling of exploding powder came drifting to his ears.

CHAPTER EIGHTEEN

THE LYNCH MOB

WYATT'S first thought was for his brother. Somewhere down there in Tombstone Virgil was in danger—the only marshal within seventy miles.

Without pausing to think he wheeled his horse off the trail, and spurred it ruthlessly over the brow of the sage-clad slope. The horse whinnied its fright. It started to rear, ears back and teeth bared, but Wyatt's strong hands hauled hard and unyielding on the reins, forcing its head down as his rowelled heels repeated the urgency of his demand. With a final protesting snort, the gelding sprang into the descent.

Down and down they went, sliding and slithering in the loose shale and crumbled rock. Wyatt leaned backwards, throwing as much of his weight as he dare to the rear, aiding the powerful hindquarters in their fight for a foothold. Twice a stunted thorn bush blocked their path, but somehow the gelding managed to slither past with nothing worse than one flank raked by the vicious thorns. Wyatt felt the spines tearing at his trouser leg and cutting their way clear into his flesh, but there was nothing he could do about it—he needed all his wits about him to keep his balance.

The horse must've tobogganed for the best part of eighty yards before it regained its grip on firmer going, its hooves striking a solid matt of roots which acted as a gentle break. It dug its rear hooves deep, found solid rock, and checked the crazy descent.

" Steady boy, steady ! " Wyatt called, feeling the shivering tremors that quivered their way across its hindquarters. He reached forward slapping the high-arched neck reassuringly, and let the reins go slack. " Find your own way, feller," he suggested as the horse calmed and gingerly shifted its weight to its forelegs.

The horse flicked its ears at the sound of his voice, blew hard through flaring nostrils and took a suspicious step forward. Gaining confidence, it walked crab-like across the line of the slope, testing each foothold before it shifted weight again, and gradually they worked their way downwards.

By the time they reached easy going Wyatt was fuming with impatience which he did his best to hide from the horse. The gunfire from the centre of town had long since ceased, but a many-voiced chorus of angry shouts, catcalls and mock Apache war-cries sounded continually in his ears.

" Get me there as soon as you can," the
marshal urged and the horse responded nobly,
lengthening its stride as it pounded over the
sun-baked soil.

Minutes later they struck the main trail
again, having saved a good three miles of winding
track by their dangerous short-cut, and were
racing at full stretch up the final slope between
the jumbled tents and wickiups of the new
diggings. As he rode Wyatt was scanning the
streets of frame buildings and tin-roofed shanties
for sign of Virgil. All he could see was the
distant mob of some two hundred men who were
milling around the main thoroughfare—until a
sudden movement by the Wells Fargo office
caught his eye. He saw a familiar, buckskin-
clad figure detach itself from the corner of the
building and peer in his direction.

" That's Cherokee ! " he cried aloud, swinging
the horse to the left and making straight for him.

" Thank Heavens you're here, Wyatt ! " the
old hunter yelled above the din of the shouting
as Wyatt sprang to the ground and came to a
stumbling halt in front of him.

" What goes on ? " the marshal demanded.

" Come inside. Virgil's there. He'll explain,"
Cherokee Watson answered briefly, and both
men pushed their way into the Wells Fargo
office without pausing to tie the winded horse.

Virgil Earp was standing to one side of the

room, with a six-gun in his right hand, while a short, dishevelled man backed the far wall with terror written plainly in his eyes.

" It's a lynching party," Virgil explained. " This crazy little tin-horn pulled a gun on the mine engineer at Charleston this morning. The Charleston marshal arrested him and decided it wasn't safe to jail him there when he heard talk among the miners that a lynching party was being assembled. He stuck him in a buggy and made for Tombstone, but the horses failed on him, and if I hadn't come along on a fresh horse I guess that would've been the end of the story."

" What d'you mean ? " Wyatt queried. " Speak plainly, Virgil, and keep it short."

" I picked him up, put him on the horse behind me and brought him into Tombstone with the lynchers hard on my tail," Virgil blazed. " Is that plain enough for you ? "

" Plenty," Wyatt answered coolly. " I take it the mob at the end of town doesn't know yet where you've taken the prisoner ? "

" Correct. But it won't be long before they find out. They're heading this way fast. I guess we'll have to back down and let them take him. We can't stand up to that mob."

Cherokee Watson nodded his agreement. " He's not worth worryin' your head over, Wyatt," he counselled. " He's a cheap killer, and he's headed for a neck-tie party anyway.

There's no sense in riskin' our lives to protect his."

Wyatt rounded on them both, his eyes blazing with anger. " Did I hear you right, Cherokee ? " he asked quietly.

Cherokee flinched before his friend's wrath, but he stuck to his guns. " You heard me right, Wyatt," he muttered defiantly. " He's a murderer. He shot that mine engineer in cold blood over a poker game. He ain't worth savin'."

" Then that's the last time I listen to you ! " Wyatt Earp roared. He turned to his brother. " Will you back me, or do I have to play this alone ? " he demanded.

Virgil stood up straight and met the cold grey eyes that were turned upon him. " I'll back you, Wyatt, and so will Cherokee. But I agree with him—it's madness to face that mob."

" Mad or not, he's committed a federal offence, and it's my duty to see he stands a fair trial," Wyatt flared. " There'll be no lynching while I wear a badge. Follow me ! "

By now the lynching party was completely out of hand and dangerously close. Their numbers swollen to a good three hundred by fresh arrivals from the neighbouring scrublands, the Charleston miners were making their excursion into Tombstone the excuse for looting every store and saloon they came upon in their search for the fugitive. Hard on their heels another two hundred wild and dirt-stained men were forsaking the mines and tunnels in which they grubbed for silver, and flocking to join them on what promised to be the rowdiest spree ever to be let loose on the mining town.

Wyatt Earp summed up the situation from the doorway of the Wells Fargo building.

" We best cut out through the back way," he ordered, his restless eyes searching the nearby blocks for some suitable place in which to make his stand. " What's that building over there, Virgil ? " he demanded as his gaze settled on a long, low shack that jutted out from Allen Street and backed on to open ground.

Virgil peered round the door. " That's Vogan's Bowling Alley," he said at once.

" Right. That'll suit us fine. Get your prisoner across there as fast as you can. Cherokee, you guard the rear, while I hold the front. We'll show these hoodlums who's boss in Tombstone ! "

Virgil obeyed at once, hustling his prisoner out through the back door, and keeping to the lee of the buidlings while he awaited his chance to make his dash for Vogan's. Cherokee slipped out behind him, his Navy Colts drawn in readiness to protect the town marshal and his prisoner with covering fire.

But Virgil was barely halfway across the street when the mob spotted him.

" There he is ! " came a yell from a score of throats. " After him, boys ! " And with the ferocity of a pack of starving timber-wolves the miners broke into a run to head him off.

And then Wyatt Earp acted. He seized a Wells Fargo gun from the rack beside him, checked it hurriedly, and hurled himself out into the path of the miners.

Tall and dignified in his long black coat and dust-stained shirt, he took his stance in the centre of the road, the shotgun cradled carelessly in his arms.

" Back up ! " he cried at the top of his voice. " There'll be no lynching in Tombstone while I'm alive ! "

The leading rioters checked in their strides, but the rest of the mob were out of control, plunging forward like stampeding Longhorns.

" Get out of our way, Earp ! " they yelled, but Wyatt held his ground, the double barrels of his borrowed gun rising slowly and easily into firing position. Out of the corner of his eye he saw Virgil reach the Bowling Alley, and spotted Cherokee hobbling fast for the rear of the building.

" Back up ! " he roared again, but his voice was drowned by the screams and catcalls of the lynchers. The din was terrific, beating on his eardrums until he was deafened and his head felt as if it would burst. He glanced quickly over to the door of Vogan's again, saw Virgil had disappeared inside, and began to edge towards the sidewalk himself.

The crowd was all around him now, howling threats and demands for the prisoner, but Wyatt still kept the shotgun level at his waist, ready to blast the first men who moved too close.

He felt the back of his heel touch the bottom board of the sidewalk, stepped up quickly, and braced himself against the door frame.

" Get back ! " he yelled as a swarthy, bearded miner moved to follow, but his voice was hoarse, and hardly rose above a croak. Another man moved to follow the first, and then a third and a fourth.

Wyatt's brain was racing. He heard Virgil's voice behind him, pleading for instructions, but the noise of the mob was almost too much for him—he just couldn't think straight !

And then he saw a sight that brought calm sense flooding back to his tortured mind. Straight across the street, lounging idly against a post stood Johnny Behan—Sheriff of the County ! Fully armed, his badge displayed plainly on his shirt front for all to see, the Sheriff simply stood and watched the lynching mob with an easy grin on his face, and didn't make a move to aid the two peace officers !

Wyatt felt a wave of cold reason pass over him. It was as though he had suddenly dived head first into a mountain pool. He rapped out an order to Virgil over his shoulder.

" Take your prisoner to the rear, untie his hands, and if this mob gets me give him a gun and let him take his chance with you and Chero-kee," he instructed his brother.

" *A leaderless mob is the most dangerous.*"

The words heard long ago when he first came West suddenly sprang into his mind. Of course ! He had been a fool not to think of it before. Wyatt faced the frenzied mob, searching the faces of the men who were now within feet of him. There was no one man who stood out as the leader—no one man with whom he could match his wits. If only he could find such a man he stood a chance, a very slim one, but it *was* a chance.

Wyatt's eyes picked out the burly figure of Dick Gird, owner of the biggest mine in Tomb-stone territory. He was in the front rank of the mob, yelling like a maniac.

" All right, my friend," Wyatt thought. " I'll make you the leader—then we shall see what happens."

Without pausing, Wyatt stepped forward and rammed the barrel of his sawn-off shotgun hard in the mine-owner's belly.

" Take your men back to camp, Mr. Gird," he yelled in the man's face, " or I'll put a charge of buckshot clear through you. And then I'll take two men at least alongside of you with the second barrel before I die ! "

Dick Gird glanced apprehensively at the gleaming barrels, then up at the marshal's scowling face.

Wyatt saw a flicker of fear in the man's eyes, and jumped at this first sign of weakness.

" I mean it, Gird ! " he roared. " One move forward and I'll blast you. Call your men off and learn some sense. My prisoner will get what's coming to him all right, but it'll be after a fair trial. There'll be no lynching. Come on, man—move ! Take your men and get back to camp ! "

Dick Gird found himself staring deep into Wyatt's eyes. He saw his own reflection in the pupils and read Death there as well. His own eyes widened, and beads of sweat formed on his top lip.

" I guess you're right, Marshal," he whispered, so faintly that only those closest to him heard a sound. He turned abruptly, shouldered his way through the crowd. " Come on, boys ! " he shouted as he moved. " Break it up. Leave him to the marshal ! "

For a second or two nothing happened. The noise of chanting and cat-calling still rose up from the rear of the five hundred massed men. Then, suddenly, the men around the mine-owner moved to follow.

Wyatt Earp let out a heart-felt sigh of relief, but he wouldn't relax until he was sure he had won the battle of wits.

" Go on ! Move ! " he yelled at the men nearest to him. " Do as Gird says." He picked another three men he knew by name and swung his gun on them. " Rodgers ! Schmidt ! Harris ! You heard me ! *You're* booked for Kingdom Come next ! "

As though by magic the front rank of the mob dissolved, backing away as quickly as the rear ranks would allow. The marshal had won his battle—single-handed against five hundred desperate men !

CHAPTER NINETEEN

MESSAGE FOR THE CLANTONS

OVERNIGHT Tombstone Territory woke up to the fact that it had a marshal who feared nothing and nobody. But the lawless element had more to learn—the hard way—for Wyatt Earp was not one to rest on his laurels. His sight of Sheriff Behan grinning at the lynching mob without lifting a finger to help had driven home to him the need for following up his success by poaching on that worthy's preserves. If Johnny Behan wouldn't act against the outlaws who by all accounts thronged the neighbourhood—then by Heaven he would !

But first Virgil needed some help in his job as Town Marshal. Wyatt grinned happily to himself. There was a lot to be said for wearing a federal marshal's badge. He could get himself deputised by any peace officer who needed a helping hand ! That way he could stick his nose—or his Buntline Special—into any affair he had a mind to !

Virgil Earp jumped at the chance of having Wyatt on hand. Together the two brothers set about cleaning up the streets of Tombstone,

Virgil soon proving himself an apt pupil at the art of buffaloing trouble-makers which his brother had perfected with Bat Masterson in Dodge.

" It sure does take the fight out of them ! " he chuckled as he bent to pick up his tenth victim and relieve him of his illegally drawn gun.

" There's more to a peace-officer's job than that," Wyatt warned. " You've got to out-think the hoodlums as well as out-fight them. Try to gauge what they're going to do before they go into action. That way you'll save a mighty lot of gunplay. Many times a fist is a better weapon than a gun, and the strongest medicine of the lot is the scorn of their fellow men."

" How d'you mean ? " Virgil asked.

" Humiliation hurts worse than anything," Wyatt told his brother. " Nine tenths of all gunplay is boasting. Hurt a man's pride and he's no longer got anything to boast about. Let him know you can take him with one hand tied behind your back and he won't risk being made to look a fool again. Bat and I found a nice peaceful way of keeping order back in Dodge that worked on that principle."

" What was that ? "

" We set up target-shooting booths all over town, and invited the visiting Texans to try their luck. Then we went round from booth to booth, gave them a display of what we could do, without any boasting—and left them to think it over. You'd be surprised how many of them looked the other way when we were on the warpath!"

"Talking of the war-path," Virgil broke in. "That reminds me. Doc. Holliday overheard some wild talk up at the Oriental last night. Seems some of Clanton's riders slipped into Town for a spell of gambling and Doc.'s expecting trouble. He wants to see you right away."

Wyatt frowned. If Doc. Holliday couldn't handle a spot of trouble for himself it must be something big. He cocked an eye at Virgil.

"I thought *you* were Town Marshal?" he remarked dryly.

Virgil Earp opened his hands expressively. "I am, but as far as Doc. Holliday's concerned there's only one man he's got any time for. That's you. You'd best hear what he's got to tell you."

Wyatt found Doc. Holliday without any trouble. Although it was barely noon, and the ornate, over-furnished saloon was practically empty of thirsty miners or cowboys, the gambler was seated at a massive baize-covered table with a pack of playing cards in his delicate hands.

"Hear you want to see me, Doc.," Wyatt stated as he pulled up a chair across from the gambler and rested his folded arms on the table-top. " What's eating you ? "

Doc Holliday didn't look up, his hands still played restlessly with the cards, twisting and turning them, cutting, shuffling, and restacking them as he continued his endless practice.

" Would you like to get acquainted with some of Clanton's boys ? " he asked eventually in his drawling Southern accent.

Wyatt smiled. " Sure would," he said casually.

" Then come in to-night. They're aiming to do their gambling with guns. I thought you'd like to know."

" Thanks, Doc. I'll be around." Wyatt rose slowly to his feet. " Is there anything else, Doc. ? " he asked quietly.

Doc. Holliday raised his head and stared at the marshal. " No. Should there be ? " He sounded puzzled.

A twinkle appeared momentarily in Wyatt's eyes as he moved to leave. " Only a question of the gun at your waist, Doc.," he commented with dry humour. " I thought maybe you wanted to put it in the rack. The only gunplay in this township will be done by Virgil or me. Don't forget it." And with that the marshal ambled out of the saloon without a backward glance.

For a full two minutes Doc. Holliday stared after Wyatt's retreating figure. His hands had stopped their restless weaving, and the cards were stilled. The bartender, watching nervously from the other side of the room, felt certain the little man was about to explode with wrath, but instead the Doctor let out a deep sigh, reached down beneath the table and flicked his nickel-plated Colt out of his waistband.

He sat looking sadly at the six-gun for a while, then stood up suddenly and walked with quick confident strides to the gunrack beside the bar.

" You've just seen History made in this saloon," he scowled at the bartender. " There's only one man on this Earth could make me park my gun against my will—and he didn't even wait to see me do it."

Without another word Doc. Holliday returned to his table and picked up the pack of cards. Presently a gruff chuckle escaped from his moustached mouth. It came again, and then the little man was laughing until the tears rolled down his face.

" What a man ! " he spluttered. " I can't wait to see what he does to those gol-durned, good-for-nothing, boasting, bat-eared Clanton boys ! "

Darkness had come to Tombstone with the suddenness that a plainsman could never get used to in a month of Sundays. One minute the sun was burning angry and red above the

rim of the Dragoon and Mule mountains that
marched their way across the horizon—the
next minute it had disappeared from view and it
was night.

Wyatt Earp picked his gunbelt from the wall-
hook of the room that he shared with Virgil and
buckled it about him.

" Be back in a little while," he told his brother
as he made for the door. " I've got a little job
to do for Doc. Holliday."

Virgil Earp raised an eyebrow. " Want any
help, Wyatt ? " he asked.

Wyatt shook his head. " No thanks. Just
routine. See you later."

When he reached the Oriental the marshal
of Tombstone Territory found it ablaze with
light. The sound of raucous laughter came
to his ears, mixed with the occasional shouts of
triumph as some lucky winner saw his number
come up on the roulette wheel, or drew the
winning card in a game of chance.

The place was packed to the doors with miners
and townsfolk. Some wore their best clothes,
carefully pressed drain-pipe trousers, nattily
knotted cravats and ties, and well brushed
bowlers or stove-pipe hats. Other men had
obviously hurried to the welcoming warmth and
gaiety of the saloon straight from the mines.
They wore dungarees, dirt-stained vests and
slouch hats, and their cheeks were grimed with

dust and dried sweat. They held their cards and glasses with hands calloused from long hours of swinging a pick, or wielding a heavy shovel ; their talk was rough and picturesque, and their manner as hard as their muscles.

Wyatt surveyed the scene from the shadows of the main door. He noted every man in the saloon, placing him as miner, townsman, storekeeper, horse wrangler, or travelling salesman, and all the time searching for some man that he would know as a rider from the badlands— from the desert lands that were the home of the outlaws.

Satisfied that the expected men had not arrived, he slipped in quietly through the back entrance and seated himself against the rear wall, where he could watch the main door and check all who came or went.

He had been there a full hour before the batwing doors swung wide and half a dozen hard-faced men in chequered shirts, narrow trousers of black and blue broadcloth, and high-heeled riding-boots crowded through, blinking in the sudden glare of the oil lamps and the great glass chandelier above their heads.

" Here they come," Wyatt muttered to himself, noting the heavy Navy Colts and well-filled cartridge belts at their hips. He saw the leader swagger forward, brushing past the men who lined the bar as though they were of no account.

The others followed, demanding drinks in loud, domineering voices, pushing their way forward out of turn.

The first man paused when he reached the middle of the room, sneering his contempt at all and sundry. He stood with hands on hips watching the silent intentness of the play for high stakes at Doc. Holliday's poker game, lost interest, and turned his attention to the noisier games in progress at adjoining tables.

Wyatt Earp sat where he was, taking it all in, but neither saying nor doing anything to draw attention to himself. His eyes were wide awake, following every move the big man made.

" Deal me in on this game ! " the newcomer demanded brusquely to the nearest banker.

" The table's full. All hands are taken," the dealer told him, nodding to indicate the other players.

" Is that so ! "

With a pounce that would have done credit to a mountain cougar the man crossed to the table, lifted a miner bodily from his seat, dropped him to the floor like a sack of flour, and took his place.

" Deal me in," he roared again, completely ignoring the man he had unseated.

Nervously the gambler dealt the cards and the play continued, an ugly silence descending on the room as all turned to watch.

Wyatt still sat where he had placed himself, but his tail coat was hanging to one side now freeing his Buntline Special for immediate use should it be needed. For a moment he was tempted to rise and demand the surrender of every gun on view, but he resisted the temptation. There was plenty of time to see about that later. If there was going to be any resistance it would be safer to tackle the men when they left the saloon —otherwise innocent men might die in the crowded room.

Slowly the game proceeded, hand after hand being dealt, and all the time the big man grew more truculent.

" Deal me another hand like that and I'll blow your cards clear through you ! " he cried, slamming his Colt hard on the table top with a force that made the counters jump.

Wyatt heard the challenge, saw the gun appear —and then acted, fast. In three long strides he was across the room to the table. He leaned forward, grabbed the man by the ear, and hauled him out of his seat.

The cowboy screamed with pain as the marshal's fingers bit deep into the lobe with merciless pressure. He felt Wyatt's free hand flick the six-gun from his holster and heard it skid along the floor. Next minute he was stumbling blindly for the door, led forward by the ear like a naughty schoolboy.

" Get out and stay out ! " Wyatt ordered as he booted his prisoner into the dust of the street.

A muffled cry of anger from the bar brought him swinging round with his Buntline cocked and ready in his hand—but he was too late. Doc Holliday was in action before him.

" Throw 'em up ! " the little man shouted from beside the gunrack where he had dived at Wyatt's first move. In his right hand the nickel-plated gun glinted expectantly.

" Thanks, Doc.," Wyatt grinned as he collected the undrawn guns from each man's holster. " Seems I'm always in your debt."

" A pleasure, Marshal," the little man acknowledged with Southern courtesy.

Wyatt put the last of the guns on the table beside him and surveyed the five men with hard contemptuous eyes.

" So you're the best Clanton can raise," he sneered with biting sarcasm. " You're not worth throwing in jail. Go back to Clanton, and tell him Wyatt Earp said the next time he sees a Clanton or one of his men in Tombstone with a gun at his waist there'll be no arguing. It'll be shoot on sight, and shoot to kill. Now get out of here and don't come back ! "

" You ain't heard the last o' this ! " one of the men snarled over his shoulder as he passed out through the doors and made hastily for the hitching-rail. "Clanton won't stand for it!"

Wyatt Earp laughed. "Good!" he called to the retreating horsemen. "Perhaps he'll do his arguing in person next time. I'll be happy to oblige him at any time."

So it was that Wyatt Earp climbed into bed that night with the feeling that he had made the first move towards his final target in Tombstone Territory. He had thrown out a warning to the Clanton gang in such a way that it was also a challenge—and one that could not be ignored.

"Now all we've got to do is sit back and wait for Old Man Clanton to make the next move," he grinned happily to Virgil as he reached for the lamp and blew it out. "I've put the ferret in the hole, and now all that matters is which way the rabbit bolts."

Virgil wasn't so pleased. "I wish you had thrown those men in jail, Wyatt," he complained. "They're safer under lock and key for a while."

Wyatt disagreed. "I'm out to smash that gang for good," he said firmly. "They've been allowed to roam the whole State of Arizona committing every crime in the calendar without anyone to stop them. With Johnny Behan refusing to act, and all witnesses either killed or frightened into keeping quiet, we can't do a thing. But the minute they make a move against me personally I can pin them to a definite crime and let the law take its course."

Virgil was still unimpressed. " All you'll do is get yourself a bullet in the back," he warned. " Old Man Clanton's too wily a fox to come out in the open. He's so smart that he can walk through the streets of Tombstone, Charleston, Tucson, or any town in the State of Arizona quite openly without fear of arrest—even though he's known to be a killer, a bandit, and a rustler. There just isn't any proof that'll stand up in a court of law. If he moves against you he'll make durned sure there are no witnesses, and no proof of any kind. Don't get careless, Wyatt. Clanton is no fool."

" Nor am I," said Wyatt evenly as he rolled over and fell sound asleep.

But Fate plays strange tricks at times, upsetting even the most carefully laid plans. To Wyatt Earp's intense annoyance the news came to Tombstone that Old Man Clanton had been killed over the border in a running gunfight with irate Mexican cattlemen when he was surprised rustling cattle.

" Just my luck," Wyatt complained bitterly. " I was looking forward to matching my wits with that old coyote."

" Don't you fret yourself," Cherokee Watson answered wisely as he loaded his Wells Fargo gun and prepared to climb aboard the heavily laden bullion coach that stood under armed guard in the main street of Tombstone. " Clanton's boys are just as wild as the Old Man himself. If you ask me they'll try and outdo each other in a battle for leadership of the gang from now on. You mind how you go while I'm away, Wyatt. You can't be too careful about that bunch."

" And don't you go to sleep on the back of that coach, Cherokee," the marshal retorted with a grin. " You've got eighty thousand dollars' worth of bullion on board."

" Pah ! " the old man stormed, wincing a little as he knocked his gammy leg against the side of the coach. " It'd take more than the Clanton outfit to stop us gettin' through to Tucson."

CHAPTER TWENTY

THE BENSON STAGE

CHEROKEE WATSON was feeling irritable. Twice on the journey through the highlands he had banged his injured leg against the rack that held the baggage secure to the roof of the stage-coach. For days he had been feeling twinges of pain from the old wound he had received on that first day in Ellsworth, long ago, and now it was really beginning to hurt with a dull aching pain that spread right up his leg, and seemed to affect his spine.

" I guess I ought've listened to Doc. Samuels," he was forced to admit as he stirred restlessly in an endeavour to find the most comfortable position. " That hoss-doctor knew what he was talking about after all. I should never have taken on this stage-guard job."

" You all right, Cherokee ? " came the voice of the stage-driver from the darkness ahead of him.

" I'm all right, Bud," Cherokee yelled back. " But I wish that gosh-durned moon would come up. I can't see a thing, an' all the time I'm bumpin' up against somethin' in the dark."

" Won't be long now," the driver called.

" The clouds are going over. It'll be as light as daytime in half an hour."

" 'Bout time too," the old man grumbled. " Where in tarnation have we got to anyway ? "

The driver chuckled in the darkness. " About six miles out o' Benson. Won't be long now afore we get some hot coffee inside us."

Presently the clouds did in fact disperse and the pale moonlight came flooding down upon the trail, throwing long shadows from the cactus heads far into the desert. An owl hooted close by, and was answered by its mate.

" That's odd," Cherokee muttered half to himself. " What in tarnation's an owl doin' way out in the desert ? "

The words had barely left his lips when two rifle shots crashed out from the left, to be followed by a third and a fourth. With a muttered oath the old man threw his rifle to his shoulder and fired at the vague shapes that loomed up at him out of the dense shadows. He heard the driver yell to his horses as he fired again, and the coach gathered speed.

" Use your whip, Bud ! " Cherokee shouted above the noise of the flying hoofs. " I'll keep 'em off."

But he spoke too soon. A fusilade of shots blasted out from the cover of the rocks to the right of the trail. The driver gave one gasping cry and toppled from his seat.

Cherokee discarded his rifle, grabbed for the Wells Fargo scatter-gun, and sprayed the rocks with twin charges of buckshot. His only reward was a yelp of pain, and a further burst of firing aimed at himself. He stumbled forward, the pain in his leg forgotten, steadied himself on the top of the swaying coach, and jumped for the driving bench.

He landed awkwardly with a jar that sent an agonising pain flashing through his leg. He grabbed wildly for the rail behind the bench, misjudged the distance and fell forward—straight for the gap between the hind pair of the frenzied team. For a split second the old man caught the flash of galloping hoofs beneath him, heard the crackle of rifle and revolver shots behind— then his head struck something hard and un-yielding and he knew no more.

Back at Tombstone Wyatt Earp was in one of his restless moods.

" It must be the weather, or something," he apologised to Virgil as he paced up and down the little room they shared. " I just don't seem able to settle to-night."

" It's probably because brother Morgan's due in from Tucson," Virgil remarked, stretch-ing lazily like a cat. " He shouldn't be very long now—the stage should arrive before morning.

They'll make good time with the moon as bright as it is."

Wyatt nodded absently. Virgil was more than likely right. He was looking forward to the reunion with his youngest brother with a deep pleasure. Although he didn't like admitting to favouritism of any kind he knew deep down inside him that Morgan, who could have passed as his twin, was his favourite brother. Perhaps it was their similarity of looks and attitude to life ; or maybe it was simply that they understood each other better than the other Earp boys did. Anyway it would be great to have the youngster with him in Tombstone, where he could keep an eye on him, and hear his ready laugh. They would certainly have a lot to talk over, just as he and Virgil had when Wyatt first came to the mining camp from Dodge.

As the time ticked slowly by Wyatt grew more uneasy. He glanced at the clock on the mantelshelf. "That stage ought to have been in by now," he muttered. He looked over to the second bed and smiled to himself as he realised that Virgil had fallen asleep, fully clothed. "You'd sleep through a cloudburst," he chuckled to the sleeping form.

He walked to the window and peered out into the moonlit plaza. Far to the east the great black ridge of the mountains was transformed into jagged mounds of glass by the silver light, and bright stars twinkled overhead. It was a beautiful night all right.

And then, as he idly studied the outlines of the false-fronted stores and dwelling-houses across the plaza, a single light caught his eye. He looked more closely and saw that it came from a building at the far end of the town.

" That's the telegraph office ! " he said aloud. " There shouldn't be anyone on duty at this time of night. The clerk lives in the rooms above, not on the ground floor."

" W . . . w . . . what was that ? " Virgil Earp had woken suddenly at the sound of his brother's voice.

" Light in the telegraph office," Wyatt snapped. " I'm slipping out to see what goes on over there. Coming ? "

Virgil was wide awake now. " Sure," he said briefly, reaching for his hat.

The two brothers ran swiftly down the main street, their footsteps almost silent in the thick dust. As they ran they made out the silhouette of a man's head bent over the telegraph bench.

" The safe's under that bench," Virgil said grimly, and Wyatt saw his brother's gun spring into his hand as he increased his speed.

Running hard the two marshals reached the office together, flung open the door—and found themselves facing the startled telegraph clerk whose hand was still poised over the transmission key.

" What goes on ? " Virgil demanded.

The man gulped twice at the sight of the marshal's gun. " Call from Tucson ! " he exploded angrily when he found his voice. " For heaven's sake put up that gun, marshal. You frightened the living daylights out o' me ! "

Virgil blushed to the roots of his hair. " Sorry," he apologised, slipping his six-gun back into its holster.

" Anything important ? " Wyatt Earp inquired sheepishly as he avoided his brother's eyes.

" I'll tell you in a minute," the clerk snapped. " They're transmitting again now." He bent to his work, his pencil flying as he jotted down the message.

Wyatt Earp glanced over his shoulder. What he saw made him gasp.

BULLION COACH ATTACKED. DRIVER AND PASSENGER KILLED. GUARD INJURED. INFORM LAW OFFICERS.

" That's all," the clerk told them. " Good job you two marshals came here after all. You saved me a walk."

But Wyatt and Virgil were in no joking mood. " That's Cherokee's coach ! " Virgil cried.

Wyatt nodded grimly. " Quick, man," he rapped out at the telegraph clerk. " Find out when this happened and where—exactly."

The man took one look at the marshal's face and bent hurriedly to his key. His fingers fairly flew as he tapped out the demand, and within minutes the reply was flashing back through the ether :

ATTACK SPRUNG NEAR DREWS RANCH. SIX MILES OUT OF CONTENTION ON BENSON TRAIL.
THOUGHT TO BE WORK OF CLANTON GANG.
BULLION SAFE.

As they deciphered the message the sound of galloping hoofs drummed on their ears. All three men looked up from the bench.

" That's the incoming stage," Virgil announced.

"Morgan's coach," Wyatt Earp grunted. " He's just in time to join the posse ! "

The hoof beats grew louder and louder, and with them came the jingle of harness and the cries of the driver as he urged the straining horses up the incline to the Wells Fargo office.

" Come on, Virgil. We've got work to do," Wyatt called. " Saddle up three horses as fast as you can. I'll meet Morgan and pick up the rifles and a shotgun."

But when Wyatt reached the staging office he had to commandeer a fourth horse, for stepping down behind his brother Morgan the marshal of Tombstone Territory saw the lithe figure of his former Dodge City deputy—Bat Masterson!

"Now that's the sort of welcome I appreciate!" Bat laughed as the four-man posse headed out of Tombstone and made for the desert country.

"Me, too," agreed Morgan Earp. "I'm glad I came now. Trust this brother of mine to stir up some trouble on our first day in the territory."

"Save your breath," Wyatt cautioned from the back of his superb gelding. "This little outing isn't going to be easy. The trail's been cold for hours, and we may not pick up a lead anywhere."

By now the dawn was approaching fast, and the four men spread out across the trail, their horses eager to show their paces. Wyatt's gelding drew ahead with ease, its powerful loping stride fairly eating up the miles, but the other three horses stuck to their steady pace and weren't far behind when they topped the ridge that overlooked the desert country.

Wyatt drew rein. "Is there a short cut?" he asked as the others joined him.

Virgil nodded. "If we ease down through that draw, and cut across the mesquite we'll come out within a few miles of the Drew ranch. It'll be hard going but it'll save a good two hours' travelling."

"Good! You lead the way and we'll keep right on your tail."

Soon the sun was burning down on them, and both horses and riders were beginning to feel the worse for wear, but Wyatt would allow no pause for a breather.

"This is our big chance of pinning a major crime on the Clanton gang," was his only comment as he brushed aside Bat Masterson's demand for a halt. "I'm out to get those murdering hombres if I have to kill a dozen horses to do it."

"If you keep this pace up much longer, you'll certainly kill four for a start," Bat muttered under his breath.

"Quit grumbling and ride," Wyatt told him curtly, spurring his horse into the mesquite-clad slope.

Straight out across the scrubland they rode, making a beeline for the bluff behind which the so-called Drew ranch lay.

"How much farther?" Morgan Earp demanded as they approached the bluff. "I can't seem to judge distance out here in the desert. I would have sworn we were only a few miles off over an hour ago."

"Won't be long now," Virgil answered tiredly. "I've been thinking over this hold-up since we've been riding, and I'm pretty certain where that attack was sprung. If we swing west when we reach the bluff we'll be within half a mile of the place."

Virgil's guess was right. In a very short time he led the weary posse out of the scrub and pointed to the trail ahead.

" That'll be the spot," he said with confidence. " They would be forced to travel slowly over that stretch at night, and there's good cover on either side—even in the moonlight."

" Let's have a look," Wyatt Earp grunted, and led the way down to the trail.

It was Bat Masterson who found the first sign of the attack. His eye was attracted by something fluttering in the breeze. He rode across to investigate.

" Come over here," he called to Wyatt a second or two later, and there was something in his tone that made the marshal hurry across as fast as he could.

" What is it ? "

" Take a look," Bat Masterson said, pointing to the two motionless figures which lay beside the boulders edging the trail. " It's deliberate murder all right."

CHAPTER TWENTY-ONE

MAN-HUNT!

WHEN Wyatt Earp straightened up from examining the bodies of the two men his mouth was set in a hard line. " Bud Philpot, the driver, and Peter Roerig," he gritted from between clenched teeth. " Shot down in cold blood before they had a chance to draw a gun!"

Bat Masterson started to say something, but a shout from the others interrupted him.

" Riders coming up fast from Benson!" came the cry.

Both men glanced up the trail and made out a party of horsemen heading straight for them. Obscured by the dust of their own progress over the sun-baked soil, the newcomers were within a few hundred yards of Wyatt's posse before it was possible to identify a single man, but when the leading horsemen finally came into view Wyatt Earp whistled shrilly through his teeth with surprise.

" Sheriff Behan!" he exclaimed.

Sure enough Johnny Behan cantered up to them and drew rein. " So it's you, Earp," he scowled as he dismounted before the marshal.

" Come to check on your friend's work ? " Wyatt asked bitterly.

Sheriff Behan flushed. " I warned you a long time ago, Earp ! " he cried. " One more word out of turn and I'll settle with you for good."

A bleak smile broke over the marshal's lips. " I'm waiting," he answered thinly.

The arrival of the remaining horsemen interrupted them, and soon both posses were gathered around the bodies of the murdered men.

" Not much we can do here," the sheriff commented. " Whoever did this has had a good twelve hours' start, and the trail will be as cold as a mountain glacier. We'd best pick up thes boys for burial and get 'em back to Tombstone or Benson."

Wyatt Earp rounded on the man angrily. " Cold ? " he repeated. " Talk sense, man. The trail these killers took is as plain as the back of my hand. Look over there." He pointed to the base of one of the largest boulders. In its shadow lay a recent set of prints made by a riding-boot, with others etched deep into the sand close by. " That's where one of them stood with the horses," the marshal continued. " There are more tracks twenty yards farther down where another man knelt to fire a rifle, and there are seventeen empty shells on the trail where the rest of them pumped lead into the coach as it disappeared. You can do what you like, Behan, but I'm taking my men here and now and following those murdering devils until I catch up with them."

Johnny Behan sneered. " You're forgetting something, Earp," he countered. " *I'm* in charge of this investigation. No federal offence has been committed—all cases of murder come under the jurisdiction of the county sheriff. I say it's useless following these men, and I order you to leave it to me to handle how I think fit."

Wyatt's brothers and Bat Masterson realised with something of a shock that what the sheriff said was true. A United States Marshal had no power to interfere in a case of murder. It looked as if their prompt action and gruelling ride had all been a complete waste of time.

Morgan Earp looked across at his elder brother, and was surprised to see a twinkle appear momentarily in his eyes. It passed as quickly as it had come, and was followed by the barest suspicion of a wink.

" Wyatt's got something up his sleeve," the youngster chuckled to himself expectantly.

" So I haven't any jurisdiction, Behan ? " the marshal asked quietly.

" None whatsoever."

" Then that's just where you're wrong, my friend. That coach was carrying Mail. Interference with the Mails is a federal offence, and if you move one finger to hinder me in the execution of my federal duties as United States Marshal for this territory, so help me I'll arrest you and have you thrown into your own jail!" He turned to his posse then, "Come on, boys— let's ride!" he called, vaulting lightly into his saddle.

At first the tracks were plain and easy to read. The hold-up men had ridden hard from the scene of the attack as though anxious to put as much distance between them and the scene of their unsuccessful crime as they could. They made a beeline straight for the foothills of the Dragoon Mountains to the east. There they branched north-west towards Tres Alamos, and from then on trailing became extremely difficult.

For four full days the four men scoured the brush country, picking up the trail for hours at a time, and then losing it completely as the men they pursued back-tracked over barren rock, rode through flowing water, or dragged mesquite bushes behind them to hide the hoof prints of their horses.

Wyatt held grimly to his self-set task, fuming at all delay but refusing to give in when it seemed hopeless. This was no ordinary man-hunt to the marshal, it was a personal challenge. It was as though the Clantons had staged the hold-up as a deliberate retaliation for the way he had treated their men in Tombstone. More than that, it had been a callous, deliberate attack on a man who was known to be his personal friend— Cherokee Watson. From what he had learned from some of Behan's men, Cherokee was little the worse for wear. Knocked unconscious by his fall he had regained his senses to find the team in full flight, the driving reins trailing in the dust beneath them while he himself lay straddled across the traces of the rear pair. With commendable presence of mind the old hunter had retrieved the reins, pulled himself up on to the back of the stampeding horses, and managed to check the mad career before the coach, with its load of bullion and passengers, could overturn.

" I'd like to hear what Cherokee has to say about the Clantons," Wyatt chuckled as he pressed on into the barren land above the San Pedro River. " He must've had the fright of his life ! "

A cry from Virgil broke into his train of thought. He wheeled his horse and rode across to where his brother was pointing out tracks in the soft mud beside a narrow creek.

" One cow pony won't be going much farther," Virgil said as he drew alongside. " It's lame in both hind feet by the look of these tracks. The others went ahead and left it here with its rider— and not many hours ago."

Wyatt examined the tracks carefully. His brother was right. The badly lamed horse had been led from the water and headed off in a different direction from the others. This was the first real break they had had in four days !

" Morgan ! Bat ! " the marshal called. " Follow Virgil and me. We're on to something." And next moment the four riders found themselves heading in a totally different direction— straight for the crumbling adobe walls of a deserted ranch-house.

" Wheaton's place," Virgil told them as they circled the building before moving in to investigate. " These tracks lead straight to the barn by the looks of them. Have your guns ready."

But all they found at the barn was a badly injured cattle pony, hanging its head in pain as it gazed at them with a complete lack of interest.

" Where's the nearest ranch ? " Wyatt demanded.

Virgil thought for a minute. " Hank Redfield's place," he said at length. " Why ? "

" Fresh horses," the marshal grunted briefly. " We're on to something all right. Redfield's a friend of the Clantons by all accounts ! "

But at the Redfield ranch they again drew blank. Of the rancher there was no sign—nor was there any trace of the men they were after.

" Better try his brother's place," Virgil suggested, and once more the posse pressed on without pausing for the meal they had promised themselves an hour before.

Len Redfield's barren scrubland ranch lay some four miles off. With Wyatt and Virgil still in the lead the four horsemen were approaching fast when a man was seen to slip out of the back door of the adobe building, glance anxiously in their direction, and then run as fast as his legs would carry him for the brush behind the corral.

" After him ! " Wyatt cried, spurring fiercely.

Five minutes later they dragged a cowering, terrified man from the undergrowth. Across his shoulders were slung a rifle and two belts of cartridges. It needed only a glance to tell Wyatt that they were of the same calibre and make as the shells found on the trail at the scene of the hold-up.

" It's Luther King ! " Virgil Earp exclaimed. " He's one of the Clanton gang."

Wyatt's mouth was grim as he seized the outlaw by the blue neckerchief about his throat and pulled him towards him. " Where are the others ? " he demanded.

" W . . . w . . . w . . . what others ? " the frightened man stammered.

" The rest of the hold-up gang."

" I . . I . . . I don't know what you're talking about, Marshal. I know nothing of any hold-up."

Wyatt Earp lost his patience. He brought back his right hand and slapped the outlaw hard across the mouth with the open palm. " Talk ! " he spat out, but the man maintained a sullen silence.

" All right, my friend," Wyatt roared, throwing the outlaw down into the dust with a gesture of contempt. " Protect your friends if you like, but it won't do you any good. I'm taking you back to stand trial for murder and attempted robbery of Government Mails. You're headed for a hanging party if you don't talk."

A look of sheer terror filled the man's eyes. " I didn't do it, Marshal ! " he almost screamed. " It was the others. All I did was hold the horses ! "

A wintry smile broke over Wyatt Earp's face. " Who were the others ? " he demanded.

The man was about to answer when the sound of approaching horses reached them. Wyatt looked up in time to see Sheriff Johnny Behan ride in to the Redfield corral with two of his deputies !

" What goes on ? " the crooked sheriff asked. " What are you doing with this man, Earp ? "

" Keep out of this, Behan," Wyatt warned. " King has just confessed to taking part in the stage hold-up. We're trying to get a lead on the others."

Johnny Behan swung down from his horse and strode to join them. " Is this true, King ? " he queried.

" I guess so, Behan," the outlaw muttered. " This marshal feller knows all about it. But he'll never get the others. They're miles away by now, and I'm not talkin' any more."

Wyatt smiled sourly. " You'll talk all right when it comes to a hanging," he said quietly.

A sudden look of cunning appeared in Sheriff Behan's eyes. " I guess you're right, Earp," he acknowledged. " The sooner we get King to Tombstone and in jail the better. I'm arresting him for murder here and now."

" But he's *our* prisoner ! " Virgil and Morgan cried in amazement. " You can't do that, Behan."

" Can't I ? " the sheriff sneered. " Well, that's just what I *am* doing. Murder is a County offence—even the federal marshal here will agree he has no jurisdiction over a murder charge. Isn't that so *Mister* Earp ? "

For a moment Wyatt's brothers thought the tall marshal was about to strike the sheriff to the ground. Wyatt fought for control, his hands fairly itching to get at the crooked sheriff— but he knew when he had been outsmarted. " Take him ! " he snarled. " But I'm warning you, Behan. Take good care of him or you'll answer to me personally. I'm sending Bat

Masterson with you to see King at least arrives in Tombstone."

"There's no need for that, Earp. I can look after this man quite well without the help of Masterson or any of your men."

"Maybe," Bat Masterson broke in curtly, "but I kinda feel like the ride, sheriff. Let's go."

With the surrender of their prisoner, Wyatt and his brothers were forced to return to the soul-destroying tracking that had been their lot for four days and over a hundred and fifty miles of tortuous trails and barren wastes. Their meagre supplies were getting short now, and water was equally scarce. Several times they called at ranches and encampments, seeking fresh food and drink, but they received nothing but refusals wherever they asked. It seemed that the whole territory was siding with the outlaws and doing its best to put the law officers off the trail.

For ten days and more the Earp brothers scoured the highlands north and west along the Tanque Verde, Rincon and Santa Catalina Mountains, through the Oracles, and east through the Santa Cruz. They forded the San Pedro River for the second time, and found themselves back where they had started—in the foothills of the Dragoons!

" It's no good, boys," Wyatt stated dejectedly when he saw that their man-hunt was yeilding no results. " We'll have to pack in. Come on, let's ride for Tombstone. A few more days o' trailing and these horses will be dying on us."

Sadly Morgan and Virgil agreed. " You just wait 'til we can pin something on the Clantons," Virgil uttered savagely. " They're going to pay for every bruise and ache in my body. I've never ridden so hard since I came West."

" Nor me," agreed Morgan, wearily. " My belly's so empty it's more than I can do to stop it rattling."

But there was worse to come.

As the three exhausted men rode into Tombstone they were greeted by Cherokee Watson. The old buffalo-hunter hobbled towards them with the support of two sticks, his injured leg still wrapped in heavy bandages. " Thank God you're back, Wyatt ! " he cried at first sight of his old friend.

Wyatt Earp straightened in the saddle. " What's up ? " he demanded.

" You ain't going to like this," the old man answered. " Luther King broke jail the night after Behan brought him back. He's ridden to join the others, and they're reported as having crossed the border into Mexico ! "

CHAPTER TWENTY-TWO

SHOWDOWN !

" AND that ain't all," Cherokee Watson continued. " Ike Clanton, and Frank McLowery are in Town."

" What ! "

" It's true," Cherokee stated. " They're walkin' the streets, gambling in the saloons, and buyin' supplies as openly as you please, and nobody's lifted a finger to stop them coming and going as they like. Johnny Behan just says they have committed no offence that he can name or prove, and as far as he's concerned they are free to do what they like."

Wyatt Earp sat stock still in his saddle and let Cherokee's words sink in. So this was the pitch to which things had come in Tombstone ! Known killers could roam the streets at will, while the Sheriff of the County sat back and bade them " good morning, gentlemen ! " From his first day in the territory Wyatt had known that he was fated to play a big part in taming Tombstone. He had felt drawn irresistibly towards an inevitable climax, and now the end was within sight, The issue was clear now—it had become a personal showdown between him and the Clantons.

"You know what this means?" he asked his brothers.

Virgil nodded. "Guntalk," he said grimly.

"Us or them," Morgan Earp agreed.

Wyatt nodded. "I'm going to order the whole bunch out of town. If they come back it'll mean a pitched battle in the streets of Tombstone and nothing but hot lead will decide the outcome. Are you with me, boys?"

"You're darn tootin'!" echoed his brothers with glee.

Ike Clanton was adjusting the cinch of his saddle when Wyatt Earp first set eyes on him.

"That's the man," Virgil told him. "Frank McLowery's in the saloon. He'll be out in a minute. They've just picked up some supplies at the store and aim to ride back to the hills within the next ten minutes."

"Where did you learn all this?" Wyatt asked, keeping his eyes on the son of the outlaw leader.

"Over in the Oriental. Doc. Holliday told me."

"Should be accurate then," Wyatt acknowledged.

Virgil nodded. "I guess so. The Doc.'s kinda fond of you, Wyatt. He told me to tell you none of them were wearing guns—but if you ever want a spare Colt his is still in the rack. I don't know quite what he meant by that."

" I do," Wyatt grinned happily.

As they spoke, a wiry, dark-haired man clumped down the sidewalk to join Ike Clanton. On his back was a sack of canned goods. Clanton helped him sling the sack across the back of a pack-horse at the hitching-rail, and was turning to free his own cattle pony when Wyatt strolled across the plaza.

" I want a word with you," the marshal called.

McLowery muttered an oath, and Clanton stopped dead in his tracks. Wyatt took his time, walking easily at an ambling gait. " My name's Wyatt Earp," he informed them as he halted within a few feet.

McLowery stepped forward. " We've heard about you," he sneered.

" And I've heard *too much* about you, Mc-Lowery. All I've heard since I came to Tomb-stone is how you've got this territory organised for murder, rustling, thieving and every other crime men can think of. I aim to stop it—and I figure the time to start is right here and now."

McLowery guffawed coarsely. " Just listen to the marshal ! " he bellowed to his companion.

Ike Clanton sniggered. " D'you think he's talkin' to us, Frank ? " he asked innocently.

" I'm talking to you and all the rest of your

collection of range rats and two-bit tin-horns,"
Wyatt told him evenly. "And I'm telling you
to get out of this town and stay out."

McLowery stopped laughing and thrust his
unshaven face within two feet of the marshal.
"We come an' go as we please," he snarled.
"Neither you nor any of your lousy brothers will
stop us. It's *you* who're going to be run out o'
the territory—not us. You'd be dead now if I had
a gun on me, my fine friend."

"Help yourself," Wyatt offered, slipping his
second gun out of its holster butt first, but
the outlaw turned his back and sprang for his
saddle.

"We're coming in to get you, Earp," he
threatened. "Save your guns for then—you'll
need 'em."

"I'll be waiting," the marshal answered in the
same quiet tones. "Start shooting the minute
you show your face in the town limits, 'cos I'll
be gunning for you from that second."

Tombstone seethed with excitement. Wyatt's
challenge and the counter threats from the
outlaws were common knowledge within minutes
of them being issued. Men hurried from saloon
to saloon, from store to livery stable, and from
mine to smelting shed. Everywhere the situation
was summed up in one word : *Showdown*.

"I hope that marshal feller knows what he's

doing," Dick Gird muttered from the safety of his mine office. "He's got courage all right—I've never forgotten the way he stood up to us over that crazy lynching business—but he's up against the worst pack o' killers in the western states. This'll be no six-gun duel where the best man wins. It'll be a pitched battle with no holds barred."

"Or else a shot in the back when he's asleep in bed," one of his clerks stated cheerfully.

Even Cherokee Watson was worried. He trailed his friend wherever he went, a Wells Fargo gun tucked perpetually under his arm as he hobbled in Wyatt's tracks as fast as his stick would allow him.

"What d'you think you're doing?" Wyatt Earp demanded as he tried ineffectually to brush the old man off.

"Taking care you don't get shot up afore your time, my friend," the old hunter answered. "I got you into this mess, and by Jiminy I aim to see you get through it alive and whole."

"For Heaven's sake run away—you make me nervous," Wyatt complained, but Cherokee stuck to him like a leech and wouldn't be shifted.

"When d'you think they'll strike?" Morgan Earp asked as the three ate breakfast at Wyatt's lodgings.

"Straight away. They won't waste any time. Why? Are you worried?"

"No. I'm just fed up with waiting. Let's get it over with, I say."

"Me, too," agreed Virgil. "There's no time like the present."

"You won't have to wait long," Wyatt told them calmly. "Johnny Behan rode in an hour ago, so Cherokee tells me. Whenever that hombre appears it means trouble for the Law."

Wyatt turned his attention to his breakfast, tackling the eggs and bacon with an appetite that had persisted ever since his return from the unsuccessful trailing of the hold-up men. But neither Virgil nor Morgan had any taste for food. They toyed with the eggs and nibbled at the bacon for a while, then threw down their forks and hurried out into the street to keep watch.

Hour after hour went by, and still no sign of the outlaws was apparent. The tension in Tombstone was mounting with every minute. As though by instinct the townsmen seemed to know that to-day was the day selected by the Clantons to make their bid. Some men from Charleston direction even went so far as to inform their cronies that the Clantons and McLowerys were boasting openly that by nightfall of this very day the three Earp brothers, and any men who went to their aid, would be lying dead in the streets of Tombstone. Whatever the truth of these rumours one thing was certain—the outlaws were not intimidated by Wyatt's show of force, nor by his threats. Guns alone could decide the issue.

" Better keep together," Wyatt warned his brothers as he joined them on the street. " Keep your backs to a bare wall as far as possible. We don't want any of Clanton's friends taking a pot shot at us before we get into action. Check your guns and try to relax. If you can get through the waiting you'll be able to face the shooting calmly when it comes."

The town was filling up rapidly now, with men flocking in from the mines and ranches to see the final showdown with the outlaws. They crowded the saloons, jabbering and talking excitedly, or taking bets on the outcome.

" Keep off the streets ! " Wyatt called to a crowd of loungers who had taken up a grandstand seat in front of the Oriental. " I don't want any more bloodshed than necessary today."

" There won't be any bloodshed at all, Earp," came a sneering voice from the entrance to an alleyway leading into the main street.

Wyatt turned slowly and found himself face to face with Sheriff Johnny Behan.

" Behan ! " he roared. " I've been looking forward to meeting you—you conniving, protector of killers ! "

" Hold it, Earp ! I'm not armed."

Wyatt Earp let his gun hand drop. "Trust you to leave your gun at home when you come to meet me," he spat with biting scorn.

Behan flushed. "I came to tell you Billy Clanton, Ike Clanton, Billy Claiborne and the two McLowerys—Tom and Frank—are down at the O.K. Corral on Fremont Street. I've been down there and disarmed them. They're leaving town at once."

Wyatt Earp's eyes narrowed. "What trick is this?" he demanded icily.

"There's no trick," the Sheriff retorted. "It's true. They're leaving peacefully—without guns."

"That I'll never believe," Wyatt stated with conviction. "This is more of your dirty work, Behan. Get out of my way. I'm going to find out for myself."

Virgil and Morgan Earp swung in on either side of the marshal, and the three brothers, looking strangely alike in their cut-away coats and black, wide-brimmed sombreros, headed in the direction of the O.K. Corral.

Cherokee Watson hobbled forward. "Wait for me, Wyatt!" he cried, making to follow in their wake.

"Keep out of this, Cherokee," Wyatt shouted over his shoulder. "I mean it—you'll be in the way."

"Do as he says," hissed a voice almost in the

old man's ears. " Keep your eye on Johnny Behan. He's got a gun hidden in his shirt."

Cherokee Watson looked up in wonder. He found himself staring into the intense, smouldering dark eyes of Doc. Holliday.

" I'll look after Wyatt for you, my friend," the little dentist grinned as he tapped his nickel-plated Colt. " I need a little practice, and you'd do more good watching Behan." And with that the gambler took to his heels and ran hard down the street after the three Earps, his grey coat-tails billowing out behind him like some strange set of sails on a land yacht.

Doc. Holliday reached the marshal and his brothers just as they turned the corner to the corral. In so doing he walked right into the pages of frontier history. For facing the lawmen, not eight feet away, stood the outlaws—fully armed !

" Throw up those guns ! " Virgil yelled as he saw the drawn revolvers bearing on them.

Tom McLowery sprang sideways for the cover of his horse, blazing at Morgan Earp as he did so. Wyatt's Buntline flashed into view, barking its message of death at Frank McLowery as he too pulled his trigger. And then the air was thick with gunsmoke and flying lead. . . .

Morgan, his coat singed by Tom McLowery's shot from cover, dropped on one knee and blazed at Billy Clanton as he drew a bead on

Wyatt. His bullet caught the young outlaw slap in his gun hand. The six-gun dropped from the shattered wrist, but the outlaw grabbed wildly for his second gun with his left hand. He was about to fire again when both Morgan and Virgil let loose a hail of lead. Struck in the chest and the ribs, he jerked backwards, staggered a couple of steps, and fell to his knees, as Ike Clanton threw down his gun and pleaded with Wyatt not to fire.

" Start shooting or get out ! " the marshal roared, brushing the outlaw aside and throwing a shot at Tom McLowery. He was too late to save Virgil from a shoulder wound, but his bullet seared the back of the terrified horse, and it broke free from McLowery's grip and raced off down the street.

For a split second Tom McLowery stood unprotected in the open, and then he too took to his heels and tore off after the horse. Wyatt levelled his Buntline and squeezed the trigger, Doc. Holliday's Colt barking simultaneously, and McLowery fell—shot twice through the body.

But Doc. Holliday was in danger. Out of the corner of his eye Morgan Earp caught a movement from the dying Frank McLowery. He flashed around, firing hastily even as the outlaw's gun belched flame. A cry from Doc. Holliday announced a flesh wound in his neck, but

Morgan's bullet had done its work. Frank McLowery died.

Ike Clanton and Billy Claiborne had fled the battle, but the last of the Clantons—Billy—wounded in five places, still somehow clunℨ to life. He fired again, and Virgil dropped with a bullet through his leg. Calmly Wyatt flicked his gun around and hastened the dying outlaw to his fate.

The battle of the O.K. Corral was over—in thirty seconds from start to finish !

Wyatt Earp broke open his Buntline Special and blew instinctively down the barrel. He felt an overwhelming sense of sadness as he surveyed the scene. Cherokee Watson hobbled towards him with tears of relief in his eyes as he saw his old friend standing there unscathed after the fastest gunfight ever to be fought in the West. He was about to say something when the expression in Wyatt's eyes stopped him. He saw the marshal's lips move and heard one simple sentence.

" I hate killing—but there are times when the Law has no other choice," said the Marshal of Tombstone Territory.

" I know," said Cherokee gently as he took Wyatt Earp's arm and led him to where Doc. Holliday treated Virgil's wounded leg. " That's why you *are* the greatest marshal in the West."